D0045368

Reading Service Center
Fresno State College
Fresno, California 93726

Other Books by Rafaello Busoni

Stanley's Africa
Somi Builds a Church
Mexico and the Inca Lands
Australia
Italy
The Far, Far North
South Africa and the Congo
Arabs and the World of Islam
The Negro Lands and the East

The man who was Don Quixote

The man who

Don

The Story of

PRENTICE-HALL, INC.

was

Quixote

MIGUEL CERVANTES

Written and illustrated by
Rafaello BUSONI
editorially assisted by
Johanna Johnston

Englewood Cliffs, N.J.

Quotations from *Don Quixote* are used with the permission of The Viking Press, and are from the Samuel Putnam translation, *Don Quixote*, copyright 1950 by The Viking Press.

Sixth printing. . . . . . August, 1966

Library of Congress Catalog Card Number 58-13746

© 1958 by Prentice-Hall, Inc., Englewood Cliffs, N.J. All rights reserved, including the right to reproduce this book, or any portion thereof, in any form, except for the inclusion of brief quotations in a review. Printed in the United States of America.

54836–T

To the indefatigable
JOHANNA EFRON
and
Bob Hunt
who worked the bellows

The man who was

The Story of

Don Quixote

Cervantes

1

IN WHICH *we peer into the future for a surprising glimpse of our hero in middle age—and then go back to tell the story properly, beginning with his parents and his birth.*

THE YEAR IS 1603. Our hero, Don Miguel de Cervantes, gray, lean and weatherbeaten at fifty-six, is sitting quietly in a small cell in a Madrid jail. Our hero—in jail? What has happened? All in good time, my friends. We will come to that later. Right now, suffice it to say, he has done nothing wrong. He awaits the moment when the authorities will discover this fact; meantime, he is perfectly happy. He is writing a book!

Day after day, Don Miguel bends over the rickety table in his cell, and his quill pen scratches furiously across the paper. Now and then he stops and looks over what he has written, and he shakes his head a little.

He is amazed, himself, by what he is writing. Heroes, by universal agreement, are young and handsome—but look at the hero he has invented! A man as gray, lean and weatherbeaten as himself—and not only that, but completely addlepated too: "A gentleman-farmer so immersed in reading books of chivalry that finally, from so little sleeping and so much reading, his brain has dried up and he has gone completely out of his mind."

A smile tugs at the corner of Don Miguel's mouth. He is amused as well as amazed by his creation—"a madman seized by the weirdest idea ever conceived in the world, the idea of putting on a suit of armor, leaving his farm, and riding out to put in practice all he has read in books." Giants, maidens in distress, enchantments and wizards—the poor fellow is convinced he will find all of these, once he rides out as a knight-errant. And being so convinced, he *does* find them, paying no heed at all to clear-sighted folk who tell him the giants are windmills, and the maidens want no rescuing. As for the

1

enchantments, why, they are everywhere, the one sure explanation, always, for events that do not fit his idea of how they should be.

Light has faded from the cell now. It is too dark to write any more, and Don Miguel leans back to muse, the little smile still lurking about his lips. Where has he come from, this absurd knight of his story, this Don Quixote, riding his broken-down nag and insisting, in the face of all reason, that the world be the way he wants it to be? Is he really just a fantastic figment of Don Miguel's own imagination, born during the long, lonely months on horseback that preceded this time in jail? Or has he known Don Quixote somewhere, sometime— in reality?

Oh, never anyone who was really Don Quixote, in all of his fantastic completeness. But surely, here, there and everywhere, he has known people who partook of *some* of Don Quixote's madness. Don Miguel's memories go back and back. He remembers this person and that one—suffering all sorts of pain rather than give up some dream of what the world is. He remembers this one and that one, fighting windmills, convinced they were giants. He remembers his own father and mother, long ago, in Alcalá, the town where he was born. . . .

And now, as darkness fills the cell, the Don Miguel de Cervantes of the year 1603 fades from our view. We too go back—back to the year 1547, the year he was born.

For a long time no one knew where in Spain Cervantes had been born, and no one cared much. In the sixteenth century people took little interest in such trifles. However, when Cervantes' fame grew, when he came to be the pride of the nation, many cities claimed to be his birthplace. For a time, these claims amounted to a real race; but none of them had a solid foundation, and finally the matter was abandoned. Then, quite by chance, just a little more than a century ago, someone dug up a church register in the small town of Alcalá de Henares, which said that on the seventh of October, 1547, a boy had been baptized with the name of Miguel, the fourth child of Don Rodrigo de Cervantes y Saavedra and his wife, Leonora. The day of the birth itself is not mentioned, but this entry ended the quest for Miguel's birthplace. The eldest of the children of Don Rodrigo was a boy named for his father, Rodrigo. He was seven when Miguel was born. Then came two sisters, Andrea and Luisa, who were five and two.

Don Rodrigo, the father of our Miguel, was a nobleman (the title Don means Sir). He carried a sword in proof of his rank, and dressed as a nobleman, too, but he was poor. A nobleman was supposed to live from the income of his estates, never soil his hands with work, and if he did not want to be idle, the Church or the King gave him opportunities to be of use.

Unfortunately, Don Rodrigo had no estates to supply him with income. He was a nobleman who had to walk, stiff-kneed, in threadbare hose, who had to feign the generous gestures of the rich, though the coin he dropped in a beggar's hat was the slimmest copper of the realm. Small wonder that by the time his fourth child, Miguel, was born, he was a man with a worried face, a man who was easily irritated, sometimes harsh.

He called himself a doctor, but this too needed qualification. He had attended many lectures on medicine as a young man, but lack of funds had forced him to drop out of classes. He had continued to study on his own, but a real medical diploma he had not.

After several years of rootlessness, Don Rodrigo had decided to settle down in Alcalà de Henares. It was a boom town, and this was what attracted him. Alcalà's university, though only fifty years old, vied with the one in old Salamanca in erudition and in its number of students. Six thousand, it was told, had registered one year, and of course many more always squeezed themselves into lecture halls without paying. On the streets of Alcalà, Don Rodrigo saw all sorts

in Alcalà anybody
could be met

of important people: dignitaries, high clerics, sons of dukes and grandees. In addition, there were throngs of lesser folk who expected to make a quick penny from the spendthrift students at the University.

Don Rodrigo had been sure he would profit here. But alas, no new doctors were needed in a city which already had a brilliant medical faculty. Who would come to Don Rodrigo when the best professors were available? Perhaps he would do for a blood-letting, but in serious cases the wealthy Alcalans never thought of him. As a result, Don Rodrigo's only patients were among the poor students and poor tradesmen who could afford no one else.

It was a blow, of course, to Don Rodrigo and to his wife as well. He suffered, both because the income was so small and because he really was a good doctor, even without a diploma. He had a great love for his profession and knew as much as one could know in that time, when real knowledge of medicine was scanty. He would like to have had his skill acknowledged.

As for Doña Leonora, his wife, she suffered from still another cause. She was miserable, not because her husband doctored only the poor, but because he had to doctor at all. He was a nobleman. He was not supposed to work for financial gain. However, since it was plain that he had to if she and the family were to eat, she did everything possible to hide the fact from the world.

Obviously, it was unthinkable that Don Rodrigo could simply hang out a doctor's sign and wait for patients. He was a nobleman—which meant that if he were to have any patients, he would have to go out to them—and this, too, must be disguised. So, to please his wife, Don Rodrigo left the house each day, all dignity, dressed in

black, with beret, cloak and sword, walking stiff-kneed as a nobleman should. A footman was supposed to follow at his heels, to carry whatever he needed. Don Rodrigo had a barefoot man in rags to carry his satchel and sometimes a few books. As far as the end of the street Don Rodrigo walked slowly and stiffly. Then, turning the corner, out of sight of his wife, he became his real self, a man who cared little about the trappings of nobility. At a lively pace, he strode down to the river where his patients awaited him in their hovels and caves.

It was dark in those holes, and there were always too many people present: friends and relatives who were praying, lamenting and crying; also, gossiping neighbors who seemed thrilled to watch the dying of a human being. Don Rodrigo did his best to save his patients, but often he was too late. The poor were shy. They did not want to bother the doctor, and, of course, they tried to save the money. When they did give in and call for him, they rarely had coins with which to pay. Most often they gave Don Rodrigo a little cheese or a dead hen in payment. Sighing, Don Rodrigo would hand these poor tokens to his barefoot attendant to carry, then hurry on to the next hovel.

Meanwhile, at home, Doña Leonora was struggling with her own problems in an effort to make life a little the way it should be. Much younger than Don Rodrigo, she too had been born of a noble family, and the knowledge that she was a noblewoman went with her like a spectre through all her days.

With almost no money, and with only a half-grown girl to help, she had to keep house with a shining façade of respectability, the kind of respectability that befitted a noble's home. This was not easy in a day when almost everything had to be done at home, when very little could be bought ready-made. From early dawn till late at night, Doña Leonora, the noble lady, had to force herself to cook and brew, cure the meat, attend the smokehouse, make candles, card

and spin, weave and sew, mend and darn. There were four children after Miguel was born—four children to look after, to dress, to train and instruct.

All this Doña Leonora did. To be sure, it was no more than many women have done, and some with no help at all. Still, for poor Doña Leonora, it was doubly difficult, for she had to accomplish everything all on the sly, hiding it almost from herself. And from the time he was a toddler, there was one situation the little Miguel knew very well, as did all the children. If Doña Leonora were suddenly to stop in the middle of some task, fling off her apron, rush to a looking glass to arrange her hair and her dress, then fly to the parlor, there to snatch up a piece of needlework and to sink breathlessly but gracefully into a chair, it meant that she had spied some caller bound for the house. At such a time, with Doña Leonora posing and yawning as a fine lady in the front of the house, little Miguel, baby though he was, knew better than to make his appearance—unless he was spotlessly dressed and ready to put on his fine manners too.

And of course, when Doña Leonora went to Mass very early in the morning, she was always deeply veiled, dressed all in black, just like the Queen. Then there was no doubt that she was Doña Leonora de Cervantes, the noble lady. The world saw her as she saw herself, and except for the priest, no one outside knew what her life really was.

9

So it was that little Miguel, from the time he was a baby, lived in a world where reality had two faces. There was the reality of mamma in the kitchen, feeding him, perhaps laughing with him if she were not too tired. Then there was the reality of mamma in the drawing room, waving him away with a languid hand as if she did not know him. As he grew to be a little older, a youngster of four and five, he sometimes tagged along with his father—a father no longer cross or taciturn when he spoke with his patients, but quick and skilled and kind. Then, when Don Rodrigo left the patients and approached his own home, Miguel saw the angry, worried look return to his father's face, even as he changed again to the stiff-kneed stride.

Soon Miguel, young as he was, could see that this double life was more difficult for his father than his mother. Somehow, the world of the nobility with all its emphasis on appearances was not as important or as real to Don Rodrigo as it was to Doña Leonora. Month after month, Miguel saw his father's face grow more set, his eyes angrier.

Now, there was another baby in the house, a little brother named Juan. Then, one day, Miguel heard his father speaking in a harsh voice to his mother, saying that with five children to feed, they *must* move to a cheaper section of town. In a poorer quarter, he could give up his masquerade, really become a neighborhood doctor, and so increase his earnings. But before Don Rodrigo had even finished speaking, Miguel heard his mother cry out, "No, no!" Then he heard her talking rapidly in a low, strained voice. It was impossible, impossible! They were nobility. They could *not* live among the riffraff, with everybody in town a witness to their downfall.

So the days went by, and the months went by, and Miguel heard no more about moving. And then, suddenly, with no one knowing exactly why, nor exactly what little thing had proved to be too much, Don Rodrigo rebelled again—and this time he meant it. This absurd life of pretense had to end. It was of no use for Doña Leonora to plead, his mind was made up. No, they were not going to move to a cheaper section of town. What good would that do, anyway? He owed money to tradespeople everywhere. They were going to leave Alcalà altogether; sell the house and furniture to pay the debts, then go somewhere else to start a brand-new life.

"Go where?" whispered the stricken Doña Leonora. "Where? Where are we going?" cried fourteen-year-old Rodrigo. "Where?" echoed the girls, and little Miguel too.

But this Don Rodrigo could not answer. He himself did not know what sort of future lay ahead. He only knew that this life in Alcalà must end. Somehow or other, he must find a better way to support his family and himself.

So, in a maze of activity, the house was sold, the furniture carried away, and after all the strange excitement, young Miguel and his family got aboard a traveling coach, with only a few bundles of luggage, and set forth to find a new life.

2

IN WHICH *the young Miguel and his family travel up and down Spain, having many diverse adventures.*

L ONG, LONG AFTERWARDS—fifty years later—when the young Miguel had become graybearded and wise and sat in jail writing a book, the whole framework of that book was to consist of a man's adventures after he had set out from home with no destination at all in view—only the goal of knightly adventure.

Let us not jump to conclusions. It was not his father's story nor his own that Don Miguel was writing when he wrote of Don Quixote. He had his own reasons for sending that gentleman out on the road.

But surely, underneath those reasons, and part and parcel of the man who sat in the Madrid jail writing so steadily and so happily, were memories of that strange decade that began when he was seven —when the whole Cervantes family set forth to wander about Spain.

It must have struck the children like a thunderbolt when they first realized that this was precisely what they were going to do. It was unlikely that they would have known of their father's worryings and hesitations before he made the decision. Perhaps they thought, as Doña Leonora did at first, that they were just moving to another town. Indeed, Don Rodrigo had considered this. Then he realized that, for him, the same hurdles would be present wherever he decided to settle. Perhaps everything would be better if he could just avoid settling altogether. A fantastic thought for a man with a wife and five children? Not really—in that particular place and time, and considering the fact that Don Rodrigo was a doctor. Doctors were needed everywhere in those days. He could become a traveling doctor, going from town to town to treat anyone who might need his services, wherever, whenever he found them. Of course it would mean doing almost anything—selling pills, pulling teeth, delivering

babies, perhaps even sometimes delivering calves as well. It would mean setting himself up in the market place of a town, along with the gypsies, astrologers and soothsayers—making his pitch to the crowd even as they. But none of this bothered Don Rodrigo very much. He had always had a certain restlessness in his blood. It was Doña Leonora who worried him. How would she endure a life so unheard of for a noblewoman? Don Rodrigo wondered and frowned, and then set his jaw. She would have to endure it, for a while anyway. It was the one sure way he knew to amass some hard cash in return for all his effort.

So now, as the family jolted along over the dusty highway out of Alcalà, Don Rodrigo did have a destination in mind. They were bound for the nearest kermess.

In those days, each city and town had a kermess once a year, a kermess being a festival in honor of a saint, combined with a country fair. As a rule, the kermess lasted a week. All the peasants from

many miles around attended it. It attracted peddlers and traders from other cities, and the pilgrims, gypsies, soldiers, and all the nomads of the road who had anything at all to sell. It attracted those who wished to buy, or who just wanted to be entertained. Obviously it was a perfect place for a traveling doctor to make his pitch.

Obviously, too, it was a place to enchant the four older Cervantes children when, for the first time, they disembarked from the coach to find themselves in the midst of more color and excitement than they had known in all their lives.

Young Miguel stood beside his big brother, Rodrigo, and stared, dazzled, at all the wonders. A great city of tents and stands was built all around the town. Plainly, everyone from roundabout had been working for weeks to make this kermess the most elaborate ever seen.

The two boys could not wait to investigate everything. The girls would have liked to wander too, but Doña Leonora put her foot

down firmly, and took them into the inn with her and the baby. It was not for girls to go about unchaperoned in such a place. So Rodrigo and Miguel went exploring alone.

Staring curiously, they walked past the colorful booths where every possible kind of goods was for sale. Then suddenly Miguel was stopping. "Look!" he cried. "Look!" He was standing before a small stage where a puppet show was being performed. The puppets flounced about, hitting out at each other, while the man who was working them cried and grunted and declaimed in time with the action. Miguel, delighted, laughed aloud. Gladly would he have stayed there all afternoon, but Rodrigo dragged him on. But then there was another stage, a stage for mystery plays, and again Miguel was captured. "Look, look!" he cried once more, enraptured. For the first time, that afternoon, Miguel had found the theater which was going to mean so much to him all his life long. Once more he stood watching, completely enthralled, till again Rodrigo pulled him on.

Rodrigo had spied some poles with ropes slung between them. On these ropes daring acrobats were dancing and performing. Next, from this new delight tantalizing odors drew the boys on to the great open kitchens where whole oxen were turning on spits. Many of the oxen were stuffed with fancy extravaganza—game and fowl, the heads of which stuck out along the flanks of the mighty beasts. Along with all the food, there were hundreds of barrels of beer and wine, arranged in long piles, most of them gifts from the lords of the neighborhood, the country squires who took a personal pride in their kermess.

And all the while, along with the rich smells and the fantastic sights, there were wonderful sounds. Everywhere there were hurdy-gurdies, pipers and drummers, men playing fifes and bagpipes, viols and bass, serpents and cymbals, so that young and old could dance whenever they wished.

As for the two boys, they could hardly believe the luck which had brought them to such a place. Was it possible that they were really going to stay as long as the kermess lasted?

The next morning they watched as their father mounted a stand near the very center of all this hurly-burly, a table on the stand beside him bearing pills and ointments and other evidences that he was a doctor. He stood quiet and at ease, not making any special effort to attract attention. But when a farmer with a rudely bandaged hand stopped near the stand and looked uncertainly towards Don Rodrigo, the boys saw their father smile encouragingly, then beckon the man towards him. They watched him unwrap the bandage, clean the wound, cover it with some healing unguent, and then quickly and efficiently bandage the hand in a neat, professional style. They saw the farmer begin to smile, to nod happily, then to reach into his wallet for—wonder of wonders—real coins, which he handed very willingly to Don Rodrigo.

Now, more and more people began to stop at the doctor's stand. To some Don Rodrigo gave pills, for some he prescribed other treatments; a few he examined, then told them quite honestly that they

were not really sick, that they needed only a day or so of rest perhaps. This last treatment did his reputation as much good as anything. Word spread that here was a doctor a man could trust, no
cutthroat or crook, but an honest man.

So it was that by nightfall Don Rodrigo returned to the inn, his
wallet heavy with an unaccustomed weight of coins, *maravedis*,
reales, even a few *pesos de oro*, the golden coins which had become
so rare. His face was happy and he was already making plans for
the future. As soon as he had collected enough money, he would buy
a horse and wagon, in which they could travel from town to town,
from kermess to kermess. The family could live in the wagon. He
would make his pitch from the back of it. This would reduce their
expenses and make the whole venture more profitable. If his luck
continued as it had today, perhaps he would be able to arrange for
a wagon by the end of the week when this kermess ended.

Doña Leonora was silent, as she had been ever since her husband
embarked on this strange adventure. She was not so much horrified
as simply stunned. The whole thing was beyond her imagination,
and so she made no objection to her husband's plans, no comment at
all. She went about in a daze, doing what she had to do for the baby,
keeping the two older girls by her side, letting what would happen,
happen. It was all a dream that had no connection with her.

By the end of the week all had gone as Don Rodrigo had hoped. He had plenty of money in his pocket to bargain for a large, if not very handsome wagon, and a strong, if not very young or beautiful horse. When the kermess ended, and all the tents and stands were being taken down, the Cervantes family piled into their new wagon and started out on the road in the direction of another town which was soon to be holding its own kermess.

So began the new life of wandering, a life that gradually commenced to have a pattern all its own. Oddly enough, as the pattern became fixed, Doña Leonora seemed to grow a little happier. Housekeeping in a wagon offered no opportunity at all for fine-lady pretensions. She was out in the open, cooking for her family, tending

the baby, scolding the older children—and that was that. But even as everybody else could watch her, if they wanted to or had time, so could she watch everybody else, and now she began to see life as she had never seen it. She saw people happy and sad, overworked but still reaching for pleasure, in a way of which she had never had any notion. And she found herself gradually winning a strange, new prestige as well. Other women came to her for advice, looking up to her as the wife of the doctor and the mother of five children. Hesitantly at first, but then with more authority, she gave them the advice they asked for, and carried her head a little higher in consequence. Gradually it seemed as though the other world, the world where she was a noble lady, did not exist for her.

On one point only was she unrelenting. The girls must not run wild through the kermess as the daughters of the other carnival folk did. *Her* daughters must be reared as ladies, protected from the world. She would not let them out of her sight for a moment.

Before very long this became a terrible burden. The girls grew fretful. They whined, or sat and sulked, refusing to help her with anything. Within a few weeks Doña Leonora came to a decision. Andrea and Luisa must be entered in a convent, where they would be reared properly as well as get the education proper for young ladies. As soon as the Cervantes family came to a town which had a suitable convent near by, Doña Leonora took both of the girls to the Mother Superior, gave them into her charge, and bade them good-by until such time as the family had a settled home once again.

Then she went back to her husband, the wagon, her three children who were left—and the strange, new, restless life.

Rarely did the Cervantes family stay more than two weeks in any one place, and traveling was a tedious, time-consuming affair. The roads were bad and ruthless highway robbers made them dangerous. For this reason, many coaches and wagons teamed together to form great caravans. For protection many who went on foot—priests, pilgrims, journeymen and peddlers—journeyed along with them.

The Cervantes joined such a caravan early in their travels, and the caravan itself was almost as fascinating to young Rodrigo and Miguel as the kermesses.

Some of the caravan travelers rode horseback, others traveled in sedan chairs, a few in sumptuous carosses. It was a long train, trailing the winding mountain roads, dipping deep into cool valleys,

climbing up over the crests of the shadeless Sierras—always forward with steady determination. But there was never room for haste. The roads were clogged with traffic, and even the fastest coach had to adjust its speed to the measured step of human beings.

So they journeyed on through the Spanish provinces, through all of Castile, Estremadura, Leon, Valencia, and down to Andalusia. They trekked past wondrous castles, and Rodrigo and Miguel, walking by the wagon to ease the horse's load, gazed up at the walls and towers, wondering about the lives of those who lived there.

They crossed endless plains dotted with sheep, passed over bridges which spanned the deep gorges, descended into valleys where eternal spring kept all in bloom. Miguel and Rodrigo grew brown as berries in the wind, dust and sun.

Sometimes they did not pass a town or hamlet for days and had to spend the nights rolled into blankets. On those long stretches their food would often be nothing but hard bread, dried figs, and water from the goat-skins which tasted of the stable. It was a good day when the caravan came to a river. There they would stop to swim and wash clothing, for it was from the dirt they suffered most.

Rodrigo and Miguel enjoyed the halts along the road. If it were early in the afternoon and warm, it was wonderful to lie down in the grass of a sun-drenched meadow, perhaps with some freshly picked

23

figs to eat, and to listen dreamily to distant noises—laughter, a guitar, the braying of a donkey—while near at hand there was the soft buzzing of a bumblebee, or the chirping of a cricket.

Even if the day were windy and cool, an hour of rest had much promise. Now Rodrigo, and especially the curious young Miguel, could inspect more closely those coaches in the caravan which had happened to impress them most. They could get better acquainted with the other travelers by lingering about and asking all sorts of questions.

Never in all the world was there such an opportunity as this for getting to know all sorts of people, from the highest to the lowest. All the while the caravan was on the road, all the people who traveled with it were bound together in a warm comradeship. The comradeship might end when they had reached their goal, but in the meantime class and prejudice were wiped out.

Miguel's eye was caught by a bishop who rode in state in a sumptuous sedan chair suspended between two magnificent horses. When the caravan halted, he made his way near to the chair, the door of which was open as the bishop drank in the cool air. Eager but polite, Miguel ventured a greeting, and the bishop, bored by the long hours on the road, was happy enough to reply. Soon they were having a real conversation, the bishop and the boy.

Or perhaps it was a farmer, going along with the caravan, to whom Miguel spoke. Bewildered, the gnarled, work-worn man would look down at this boy who asked what was it like to be a farmer. What was it like, indeed? He tried to brush the question aside, but the

boy seemed so eager to know. Laboriously the farmer put his words together, like pieces of a puzzle, to tell how the young vine was planted, what to watch for when the fruit ripened, what the dangers were in the way of pests. In the end, the farmer would be marvelling himself at how well he talked with the little boy listening.

In the same way Miguel talked to traders and shepherds, grandees and colonels, forming his picture of the world, first-hand, from what they told him of their lives. Rodrigo was not nearly so interested in all these conversations as was Miguel, unless they happened to be talking to a soldier. Then his ears would prick up, his dark eyes sparkle, and he would be as quick as Miguel with his questions.

"That is the life for me!" Rodrigo would say eagerly to Miguel afterwards. "That's something worth while now—fighting the Moors as a soldier of the King." And Miguel was inclined to agree. The bishop served God, but a soldier served God *and* the King. A soldier was brave and strong against any terror or hardship, a soldier was a man who knew discipline and control.

Still, the men of God who traveled with the caravan had something very special to offer Miguel. They, more than any of the others, had the keys to the world of learning.

It was a monk, on pilgrimage, who taught Miguel his first letters. He took a burned stick and began to draw on a slab of stone. And as he did so, there appeared the words, DEOS, VIRGEN, CRUZ— *God, The Virgin, The Cross.* It was enough for a start; certainly those were the most important words. Miguel stared at the signs and repeated, "Deos, Virgen, Cruz," and traced the letters in the sand to make them his own property.

Thus, once he had begun, he could not afterwards tell how he learned to really read. It came to him almost without his knowing. Rodrigo cared little for this pastime, but soon Miguel was reading anything he could find, and any scrap of printed paper was a treasure.

As the months went by, it was the life on the road that was most full of interest and adventure. One kermess was very like another, Miguel and Rodrigo discovered—noisy, crowded and gay—but the noise and crowds were only background to the work they had to do, helping their father.

Rodrigo had the heaviest chores. He was growing towards young manhood now—fifteen, sixteen, seventeen. But Miguel was not idle either. Not every sick person came to see the doctor. Many were bedridden, and it became Miguel's job to deliver medicine and do other errands. He had a great talent for finding his way in the maze of tents and stands which looked so alike, and his slim body could squeeze a way through a crowd which seemed solid as a wall.

Also, Miguel was the one his mother called on to help with Juan and the new baby sister who had been born on the road. They were delicate, the two little ones, sweet children, but timid. Sometimes Miguel would take each of them by the hand and walk with them through the kermess; but they were happier, really, when he simply sat beside them and told them stories or made droll faces.

The months mounted into years, and still the Cervantes' wagon rolled on, back and forth across Spain. Miguel grew taller, tanned

and sinewy. By now he had seen many cities; he had been in Zaragoza, in Avila, in Carceres and Burgos, in Valencia, Malaga and Sevilla—all the great cities of the land.

And then, the year Miguel was twelve, two blows struck the Cervantes family, changing the whole atmosphere of their travels. The first blow came when both the little brother and sister took ill. Don Rodrigo used all his doctor's skill to treat them, and Doña Leonora hung over their beds in the wagon night and day. But all the medicine and all the nursing were of no avail. First one, then the other, slipped way from the life that had always seemed too loud and rough.

Doña Leonora saw them buried in the little cemetery of the town where they happened to be staying at the time. Then she went back to sit, dry-eyed and silent, as Don Rodrigo and his sons packed up the wagon and headed once more out upon the road.

A few months more they traveled, the four of them—and then, suddenly, Rodrigo deserted them. Miguel was not really too surprised when his father and mother found Rodrigo's note. He had known for the last year that his brother was growing more and more restless. After all, Rodrigo was a grown man now, and the caravan life offered him little. The help he gave his father was nothing to satisfy a strong and ambitious young man. Miguel could take over his chores easily. For himself, Rodrigo had always loved the army. As the son of a nobleman, he was eligible to become an ensign. So, one fine day, he simply disappeared to enlist—leaving the note to bid his family good-by.

Actually, Miguel could not blame Rodrigo. He was made for the army, this brother of his, and Miguel was happy to think of him, busy and eager at last, clad in leather and steel, drilling on some

27

fine parade ground. At the same time, Miguel missed him terribly. Their tastes had been different, but there was a strong bond of affection between them, a bond born of all the years they had walked together beside the wagon, along half the dusty roads of Spain.

Now, with Miguel the only child in the wagon, he tried to pretend to himself that he too led a soldier's life. The caravan, in its halts and its progress, had its own orders of the day, as regular as any soldier's. There was the endless marching, day after day—and Miguel marched like a soldier. He had to brave any weather, sleep under a wagon or on a cot, as luck provided. Like a soldier, he had to accept good fare or meager, and pleasures and duties mixed haphazardly.

For a long time, thinking of himself as a soldier was his chief comfort, but all the while, though he was hardly aware of it, Miguel was going to school as well. The road itself was his university. From the monks and priests, to whom he talked as he walked along, he learned Latin. He also acquired a smattering of mathematics. From yet other travelers he learned how to tell time at night from the position of the stars. He was handed books by Greek authors, books which at that time were almost forbidden literature. He also read some of the philosophy of Aristotle, who was not forbidden, and he struggled with the writings of St. Thomas Aquinas.

Marching along, he pondered on what he had read. He asked the monks and priests who lent him their books for their views on many matters, and then earnestly, eagerly, he tried to figure out his own.

Miguel had seen much in his young life, much of everything— misery and brutality, despair and death—but also much of love and joy, kindness and laughter. He had been a nomad for so long that it seemed to him all life was a kind of caravan, going on and on, changing and dispersing as it went, but forever reforming again, to go on. Nothing was really stable but the shape of the caravan —and above it, God, the saints and the stars. Was this enough for a philosophy of life? The monks shook their heads, but they smiled at the eager, thoughtful lad. He had a seeking mind and an honest heart. He would find his way some day to even deeper meanings.

And so the months went by, and in spite of the books and the talks, Miguel was beginning to be weary of life on the road. At the kermesses themselves, the puppet shows and the plays still kept their magic for him, but everything else about them seemed like tinsel and frippery. He began to dream of Salamanca, of the great university there. There he could range through shelf on shelf of books, not relying on the whimsical choices of traveling companions for reading fare. He dreamed of staying in one place and studying, day in and day out, really learning seriously at last.

It was just about then, when Miguel was seventeen, that Don Rodrigo also began to weary of the nomadic life. He counted up the money he had earned in the last ten years—and it was not a bad sum. He had done well enough, really, with this venture. He talked to Doña Leonora, and he talked to his son, who was almost a grown man.

Doña Leonora was startled, a little bewildered, at the thought of settling down again in a real town or city. "Remember," said Don

Madrid

Rodrigo, "I shall go on being a doctor. Even if I again wear my sword, I will keep on doctoring." After all the years on the road, Doña Leonora could hardly remember how it was that this had seemed so unbearable to her once—that her nobleman husband should work. "Of course," she answered him now.

As for Miguel, he was wild with joy at the thought of anchoring at last. Where would it be? That was the question.

"How about Madrid?" asked Don Rodrigo.

"Madrid?" echoed Doña Leonora, frowning. It was just a miserable village, wasn't it? A poor village of mud huts where pigs wallowed in the streets and gypsy children played in the mire.

"No—no, it is all changed now, Mother," cried Miguel eagerly. "The King has moved there with his court. It is the new capital now. They say it is grander than Vallodolid. The roads are all paved, there are great buildings, and long streets with big houses."

"There should be plenty of opportunity there for a doctor," Don Rodrigo said.

And so it was decided. In the year 1566, when Miguel was nineteen years old, the Cervantes family turned their horse and wagon onto the road to Madrid. And there they left them, saying good-by to the nomad life they had lived so long. They were going to become city people again.

3

IN WHICH *Dona Leonora becomes a lady again,*
Miguel joins the young intellectuals, tries baby-
sitting, and then wins a wonderful opportunity.

M IGUEL, who was given to wondering—all his life long—wondered a little about Madrid in the days and weeks after the
family's arrival. Since the town had grown into a city overnight,
with the arrival of the King building construction was far from
keeping pace with the demand. This meant that though the Cervantes had money to buy a house, no house was ready to move into
when they arrived, and they had to take temporary lodgings until
one was finished. While they lived thus, still almost like transients,
Miguel wandered about the city. He wondered why the King had
chosen it for a new capital.

Miguel had seen enough cities by now to know they were most
often built where Nature herself seemed to have arranged for a
settlement—in fertile valleys, on great river bends, or along the sea
coast where the ocean itself forms a natural harbor. But there was
nothing like this in Madrid. There was a river, yes; or rather, there
was a dry river bed. Miguel wandered along its banks, looking down
at the stones of its deep-cut channel, and asked if there were ever
water in this river. The natives shrugged. In certain seasons only,
they answered.

All around the city, there was a desert—a high plateau where
practically nothing grew. Far off to the northeast there was a wide
mountain range—a range high enough to keep most of the rain clouds
away, so it was dry everywhere around Madrid. In the daytime,
the winds were hot, but at night the temperature dropped to a point
which meant there was a chill in the air.

An odd place indeed for King Philip II to choose as his capital,—
except for one thing. Madrid was exactly in the middle of Spain,
and roads from one end of the country to the other crossed it. Sitting

here, in the center of his country, this fanatic, hard-working King could emulate the busy spider at the center of his web, pulling at a line in any direction to draw to his side whomever he wished. Not that Miguel thought of Philip as a spider, or as a fanatic either. Miguel was a child of his time; a time when kings ruled by divine right, and he had not yet seen enough of the court or the King to draw conclusions of his own. He simply thought Madrid was indeed a convenient city for a capital.

And now, finally, the Cervantes house was finished and the family could move in. Profiting from his mistakes long ago in Alcalá, Don Rodrigo lost no time in establishing himself as a neighborhood doctor. Soon he had acquired a small clientele.

As for Doña Leonora, she had agreed to this while they were still on the road and there was little she could say. But Miguel watched with amazement the change in his mother as soon as she once again found herself in a house of her own.

The acceptance of life as it was, which she had shown all the years on the road, fell away from her as though it had been a disguise. She was back in what to her was the *real* world now, the world where the fact that she was Doña Leonora de Cervantes y Saavedra meant everything.

Quickly, as mistress of a house once more, she sent for her daughters to return home from the convent. Within a few weeks they arrived.

Miguel had not seen either of them for almost ten years, when Andrea had been a gawky thirteen, Luisa still a child of ten. Now he met his sisters as two strange young ladies of twenty-three and twenty. He had looked forward to the reunion, but when he actually saw them he was taken aback.

Andrea was pale and pudgy-faced, her eyes sharp and her lips tight with self-righteousness. She sniffed discontentedly at almost everything, and she lost no time in telling them that if she'd had her way she would have stayed at the convent, taking the vows as a nun. Actually, it was all her family's fault that she hadn't been able to. It cost money to be a nun. After all, everybody knew this. Thousands of families in Spain had too many daughters and too little money, and thought it very convenient for their girls to enter a convent, thus to be rid of worldly worries. But obviously the Church could not lodge and feed everyone. So it was the custom that whoever wanted to enter a monastic order donated a gift upon entering, or willed an estate to the church in payment for board and shelter. No such contribution had been possible for Andrea, and she sighed hourly so that none would forget her martyrdom.

Luisa was not quite so depressing. For one thing, she was prettier than Andrea and a great deal more interested in the world. Especially was she interested in the possibility of a husband. But once again the lack of money made everything difficult. With no dowry to offer a man, she had to make every possible use of her charms. As a result, she was a frightful coquette, tossing her head and fluttering her eyelids whenever she thought there was someone to observe and admire.

But, changed as the two sisters were from what Miguel remembered, and different as they were from each other, they were now one with their mother in the desire for the family to maintain a respectable façade. However much all three of them might fuss and fret at home, they were united when they went forth to Mass—three black puppets, walking rigidly, looking neither to right nor left, with a shabby servant girl scurrying along behind.

Miguel watched, shook his head and sighed. What was it they gained from this kind of pretending? A pride in themselves they would not have had otherwise? How could they gain pride from

33

such an outward show? They were a puzzle to him.

But he had other matters of greater concern and interest. His one desire, born in those last months the family had been on the road, was a chance to study seriously to improve his education. The one big drawback of Madrid was that it had no university. Still, in his first wanderings around the city, he had found a group of men who quite thoroughly impressed him.

He first found them in some of the little taverns where cheap wine was for sale, or in the small new places where chocolate was served —an exotic drink to Miguel, as they brewed it then, churned to a foam and sprinkled with pepper, the Mexican way.

He was fascinated by the drink, but even more by the men he found sitting about the little tables, hour after hour, sipping their chocolate, and talking about everything under the sun.

These men were intellectuals, all of them. Some were writers, some were scholars, some had ties to the theater, but all were alike in their manners and their dress, as though they were all members of some strange priesthood or secret fraternity. Their clothes were poor and threadbare, but they wore their cloaks and capes with a certain slant so no one could fail to notice it. Some of them copied the habits of monks, in order to look even more like men of deep learning. All of them trimmed their beards very carefully, and used their hands in eloquent, sweeping gestures.

Watching them, gradually getting acquainted with them, Miguel

34

could not help but notice that, along with their mannered appearance, most of them were also quite dirty. But he told himself it did not matter, if only they would accept him and let him share in their talk and their wisdom.

He really need not have worried about their acceptance of him. Actually, these Madrid intellectuals who fancied themselves the backbone of European culture, were weary to death of each other's voices, always echoing the same opinions, the same disdain of everyone and everything. Miguel's comments were the first new thoughts that had come their way in a long time, and they made much of the young man. They paraded their own learning before him and encouraged him to follow in their steps. The playwrights of the group read their plays to him, works which both mystified and impressed him. The poets urged him to try his hand at poetry, and they praised his efforts.

All in all, it was very heady and stimulating for a while—but only for a while. Very soon Miguel began to weary of the intellectual intolerance everyone in the group displayed. He became discouraged and depressed because not one of the men could drop his pose long enough to be a genuine friend. One thing the group had done for him—and only one. It had forced him to realize how very little he had in the way of formal education. Now he realized that he did not really know Latin, only a sort of Latin dialect. He realized he had only a hazy knowledge of classic authors.

But without a university in the city, how was he to get the learning he craved? Miguel pondered, and asked questions here and there. At last he found what seemed to be an answer.

There was a professor in Madrid who took in boarders. He helped them along in their studies, in exchange for secretarial services and work around the house. Eagerly, Miguel went to see this man, called Professor de Hoyas. He found him to be a soft-spoken person, in love with the old poets and deep in a dream of rendering the minor classics into sublime Spanish. Professor Hoyas said he would be happy to tutor Miguel in Latin, as well as other studies, if Miguel would care to join the house as a *famulus*—a term which implied that, in one way, he was to be a part of the family, and, at the same time, in another way, a family servant.

Miguel found out just how confusing this kind of a position could be when he accepted the Professor's offer and moved into the de Hoyas home. The Professor's wife was busy with a whole houseful of children, and at once she saw Miguel as someone to take over all the dreariest tasks.

So it was that when Miguel was practicing the poets, scanning the rhythms with continuous nodding, Doña de Hoyas thought this an excellent time to let the young man rock the baby in the cradle while he did so. When the baby was finally asleep, there were errands to be run; the half-grown children also needed attention. And surely, for all the boarding and learning the young man was getting, he should be willing to take over the instruction of the smaller children. At night, when the children were finally in bed, when Miguel might have studied, he found it was still impossible. Doña de Hoyas had lodged him in the kitchen—which meant he had to cope with the giggling servant maid's questions while she finished up her work.

But by and large, Professor de Hoyas was a sincere man, earnest and honorable, and he took his side of the contract very seriously. Miguel had wished to learn Latin. The professor saw to it that he did.

With all this going on in the de Hoyas household, Miguel had little time for his old intellectual acquaintances of the cafés. However, he did see them, soon after the whole city was plunged into mourning for the death of King Philip's young queen, Mary. Miguel's former friends were sitting around the tables in the cafés, as always, but they were all wearing extremely withdrawn and dedicated expressions, scribbling from time to time on bits of paper. They were writing poems and other literary works in praise of the dead Queen, they told him. If Miguel wished to try some effusion of his own they would gladly take it to the publisher along with their own works.

Miguel hurried back to the Professor's, excited by the thought of appearing in print. He did indeed turn out half-a-dozen poems. When he took them back to his mentors at the cafés, they accepted them guardedly, frowned a good deal in reading them, and made numerous pointed criticisms. But several were put with the collection to be published—and before the year was out Miguel, and all of Madrid, saw the name, Miguel de Cervantes, in print for the first time.

By the time this thrilling moment had arrived, however, other events had contrived to focus Miguel's attention on something even more exciting.

Once again there was a death in the royal family. Only a few months after the death of Queen Mary, Philip's son, Don Carlos, also died. Now, not only Madrid and all of Spain grieved for the King— all of western Europe was shocked. In Rome, the Holy Father decided a mere letter of condolence was hardly sufficient for such a double bereavement. He would send a personal emissary to bear his greetings to Philip. The man he chose to be his emissary was a certain Monsignore Aquaviva, a young man of such promise that, although he was only twenty-six years old, everyone knew he would be made a Cardinal in just a few years more.

His arrival in Madrid was the signal for much ceremony. Monsignore Aquaviva came from a very old and aristocratic Spanish-Italian family, he was related to every person of influence in Italy, he was the right hand of the Pope—and in addition to this he was reputed to be an extremely charming young man.

Miguel, busy with his chores and his studies, was scarcely even an observer of the ceremonies attending the Monsignore's arrival. But after the Monsignore had been in Madrid for several weeks, the Professor came hurrying home one day with great news for Miguel.

From one of his colleagues in the city he had heard that the Monsignore was asking if anyone knew of a young man well instructed in both Spanish and Latin, who would be interested in becoming his secretary. The Professor, obviously proud of the progress Miguel had made with him, had made bold to recommend Miguel himself to Monsignore Aquaviva.

"Attend, son!" cried the old Professor excitedly. "You have an appointment with his Reverence tomorrow!"

Miguel was thunderstruck at first. Then all the possibilities of such a position began to flood in on him. As secretary to the Monsignore he would travel to Rome, live there, in the Vatican itself perhaps. He would work with, and know, all the greatest, wisest figures in the Church. Around him there would be all the glories created by the greatest, wisest minds of the past: buildings, statues, books—books—books.

By the next day, at the hour of his appointment with Aquaviva, Miguel had worked himself into a state in which it seemed this post with the Monsignore had been his one prime goal since infancy.

He had seen the sumptuous palacio, where the Monsignore was

in temporary residence, often enough. It was one of the old buildings in Madrid, very richly ornamented and massive, but now that he had to pass the guards it looked ominous, and he had to muster all his courage not to get shaky knees.

It was dark and cool inside, and a long, long corridor, with a hundred sentinels, almost made him lose heart. But in the end he stood before the last door—and then, at last, there was the important man himself.

Why had he been so fearful? Here was a grand seigneur who was only a little older than himself. And, though dressed in the imposing garb of the High Cleric, he was very human, almost cordial. With a frank smile and an inviting gesture, Monsignore Aquaviva began an easy conversation. Very soon Miguel found that he too was speaking easily, telling of his past and his present as naturally as though he were speaking with the men at the winehouse.

Cleverly and casually, with just a few key questions, Monsignore Aquaviva was finding out all about this young man named Miguel de Cervantes. Then, as Miguel stopped speaking, Aquaviva looked out the open window, seeming suddenly to be lost in thought. It was as though he had forgotten the presence of any other person, and, although his silence may have lasted but a minute or two, it seemed much longer to Miguel.

He tried to concentrate on the bust of some forgotten king in a corner. He tried to think that going to Rome was not so important after all. But the sweat gathered on his forehead all the same. Then, when he was ready to abandon all hope, he heard the Monsignore ask softly, "Would you consider coming to Rome with me?"

Miguel, barely able to prevent his suddenly released breath from sounding like a sob, bent over the outstretched hand to kiss the ring. Stammering his thanks and his promises to be all the Monsignore desired, he managed somehow to back his way out of the room and flee the palacio.

So he was appointed to the service in the Chancellery of Monsignore Aquaviva. He *would* live in the Vatican in Rome, a neighbor to the Holy Father. It had come true, after all!

That night he heard the bells ring out all the hours until it was time to rise. When he returned from Mass, a footman met him at the Professor's door and handed him a heavy purse. It contained money to pay for any purchases he might need to make before leaving for Rome. There were also instructions about when and where to meet the rest of the Monsignore's staff.

There was ample time for all preparations—no undue haste accompanied anything that Monsignore Aquaviva arranged. There was time to take the exciting news to his father and mother, time to buy more appropriate clothes for his new post, time for all sorts of instructions from his mother, time for farewells at the winehouses— entirely too much time for young Miguel's impatience! But at last the Monsignore was ready to depart. In the fall of 1569 Miguel left Madrid for the coast, where he took a ship for Naples—from which city he would journey by coach to Rome.

4

IN WHICH *Miguel discovers Rome, gets a new perspective on his homeland, and then leaves Rome— to go to war!*

ROME WAS far more than a city—it was an idea, a symbol of spiritual power, the intangible conception of splendor and glory. To Miguel, as he drew nearer and nearer his goal, it seemed almost impossible that this city should also have reality; that within its walls men should live, love and strive as in any other city.

From Naples on, he traveled by stagecoach, squeezed in among other passengers, and he hoped to get a glimpse of the Eternal City from afar. In vain! The shades of the windows were drawn tight because it was raining. Miguel wanted to shake his companions and shout, "We're coming to Rome! Open up! Only once do you come to Rome for the first time!" But no. He had to be polite and allow a few drops of rain to be reason enough to forfeit the first, far-off sight of the city.

Because of the deep-hanging clouds, evening came earlier than usual that day, and it was dark when the stagecoach jolted over the cobblestones into town. Miguel and several of the staff were expected at the mail-station where the coach stopped. From there, they were taken to their lodgings at Vatican City—that part of Rome which was built on a separate hill, where the Pope had his palace and where the buildings of the Church administration stood.

In the dark it was hopeless to try to see how anything looked. Miguel could only get a glancing impression of the labyrinthine interior of the building from the corridors down which he was led. Then he was in his room—a room all for himself, a privilege he had not enjoyed for a long time. It was a large room, sparsely furnished, but with everything in it of good quality. Most exciting of all were the windows which seemed to overlook the whole city. He could hardly wait for morning and the next day, which would be all his.

At the first dawning, Miguel sprang from his bed, opened the windows and stared out. With a tingling in his breast, he recognized certain landmarks of which he had heard all his life. There was the Tiber, Father Tiber, the famous river on which Rome was built. There were the columns and temple ruins of ancient Rome. And there, so close it almost seemed he could reach out and touch the stone, were the mighty flanks of St. Peter! The dome and nave were missing, but even so, it was a sight to quicken Miguel's breath.

Scattered here and there throughout the city were tall, squarish towers which mystified Miguel, and he wondered what was their use. Later, he was to find out that they had no use but had been built merely to boast of the power and wealth of their owners. Now, his gaze traveling on, he looked to the far distance and saw the old wall which dated from the time of the Roman emperors—a wall which girdled Rome like a too-generous belt, having been built for a city of twice its present size. Inside the wall, between the towers, and lining the river on both sides, was a maze of roofs—Rome! The Rome Miguel was going to explore—*now!*

He buckled on his sword, threw his cloak about him, and hurried down the long corridors of his new dwelling, out into the open.

The streets were still empty, the first stores were just opening their doors, and Miguel felt he could have used ten eyes and the wings of a bird to see all there was to see. Yes, yes! There were the old temples, fifteen hundred years old and in ruins, but still majestic, still a monument to man's glorious dreams. There were newer buildings, sumptuous in a different style. But why were so many of these in ruins? Miguel frowned, remembering the history of a not-so-distant past. It was his own King Philip's father, Emperor Charles V, who was responsible for much of this, without a doubt. Here was destruction that dated from the Emperor's furious quarrel with the Pope more than forty years ago, a quarrel that had led to the infamous "sack of Rome." Miguel felt uneasy, walking past the scars and ruins for which his own country must take the blame. But he saw, too, that the people who lived here were making the best of it, bringing out their sheep and goats to graze among the ruins and forsaken, half-burned palacios.

Noon came. Miguel was in the busy and noisy center of the city, and yet the streets still seemed half empty. And now once more his face was grave as he realized why this was so. The great Rome, fifty years ago a city of several hundred thousand, was reduced to forty thousand citizens at this time. War, hunger and plague had caused a great part of the population to abandon Rome, and it was the plague more than anything else which kept people from returning.

This was not the time of the great scourge when the terrible Black Death wiped out whole cities. But the plague, though no longer all-encompassing, remained a constant menace. For months it might be

The Plague

hardly noticeable, and then, like embers burning under the ashes, it would suddenly erupt, to cause the deaths of hundreds of people.

For those who had the courage to face this danger, there was still the problem of hunger. The countryside had been laid waste by the armies of Emperor Charles V. The slaughter had not spared the farmers, and food had to come from long distances, often not enough food for the city. The prices were high as a result, and many in Rome were almost starving.

As it always is with a city which has met disaster, the prosperous families had left, and others had come in their stead—people who lived from theft, and continued to loot and destroy the town.

When Miguel arrived at the banks of the Tiber he saw some of these people. Their faces seemed hardly human. Men, women and children stared at him with ice-cold, hate-filled eyes. They looked like what they were: scavengers who waited only for the night to cut someone's throat, to fight with the dogs over a rotting carcass—scavengers who thought an onion a good reward for a murder. Like rats, they lived in holes along the river; like rats, they avoided the day and blinked in the light.

Miguel felt a chill in his heart as his eyes met theirs. For a moment he thought of retreating, of simply taking to his heels rather than walk any further between these creatures who stared with naked avidity at the richness of his cloak, the shine of his sword. But he would not be a coward. He stiffened his back and walked steadily past them all till he came to a spot where he could turn off again towards the better part of the city.

All day long he continued to roam. When twilight came and he turned again towards the Vatican, he was numb from too many impressions. He had a need to harmonize all that he had seen with the ideal image of Rome which he had borne within himself. He had expected to feel everywhere the predominance of the Church, a magnificent dignity, and the presence of so much ugliness came as a surprise. He had to forget his fantasies and accept the fact that this city was alive and busy. He had to realize that in spite of ruins, hunger and crime, Rome was still more lordly than anything he had seen thus far. He sensed this truth, but it was hard to understand— that the real and the ideal could be so far apart, and yet still the real could be part of the ideal.

A few weeks went by and Miguel began to feel more at home. He hesitated to admit it, but he felt freer and more at ease than in Spain. This too was hard to understand. Here he was, living as a next-door neighbor to the Pope, in an area where the influence of the Church was constantly in evidence. And yet he felt no constraint at all in this religious atmosphere.

In Spain religion was a serious affair. There were pomp and luxury in the churches, but rarely a smile on the face of a priest. Here in Rome Miguel met priest after priest who seemed genuinely serene and light-hearted—men, who, moreover, had interests beyond their religious calling; an understanding of literature, and an awareness and an appreciation of art that enabled them to judge a painting or a piece of sculpture for its beauty.

In Spain, the presence of religion meant the presence of fear. A thoughtless word, or a laugh while church bells rang, could lead to a life without laughter from then on—for in Spain there was always the shadow of the Inquisition. This was the court, constantly in session, created to judge and punish every infraction, both minor and major, of proper religious behavior. For the most trivial kind of offense a man might be condemned to wear the San Benito, an ugly smock covered with grotesque signs. For any offense the judges considered really grave, there was the terror of the *Auto da fés*—the public burning of condemned persons.

In Rome, too, the Inquisition reigned—or so men said; but it was nothing like that which Miguel had known at home. He heard of no *Auto da fés,* and among the hundreds of pilgrims who visited the city day after day, he saw not one who wore the San Benito. Of course there were those among them who saw Satanas on every corner, and who cried nothing but "Woe! Woe!"— men who went barefoot and dressed in skins, and prophesied the end of the world. But here in Rome, these desperate fellows were not taken seriously. They were regarded as uncouth, deplorable creatures who had somehow become confused by phrases they failed to truly understand.

As Miguel talked with one Roman after another in the course of his work for Monsignore Aquaviva, he found that these men regarded his own fellow countrymen in somewhat the same amused and tolerant way. Oh yes, the Spanish priests were very zealous and industrious indeed, but so narrow and provincial. What a pity they felt it necessary to despise all the joys of this world in order to give any charm at all to the hereafter!

So it was when the talk turned to Spanish might and power. Miguel, entering the Monsignore's study with papers for his Reverence to sign, would linger to listen, a little stunned and unbelieving of what was said by Aquaviva and his callers. All his life long Miguel had been nurtured on the glory of Spain's holy wars, the importance and the unquestioned right of these punishing excursions.

Here, though no one denied the power of Spain, these constant wars were considered bizarre and romantic. Men thought it a little out of place for Spain to fight all over Europe as the self-appointed Defender of the Faith. Many were quite blunt, saying Spain had overstepped her domain, and that her acts of atrocity in the Netherlands, or in Mexico, all in the name of the Church, actually did the Church far more harm than good.

Miguel thought of his own brother, Rodrigo. When last heard from, Rodrigo had been in the Netherlands, fighting in just such a war as these men decried.

"How much wiser," he heard Aquaviva sigh, "to stop this constant blood-letting, which only weakens Europe—and save that strength for a day when it may be needed—against the Turks."

Yes, every day, every hour, Miguel felt his old values and standards toppling, new views looming up to take their place. This business of the Turks, for instance. At home, the Turks were heathens, and that was that. Here, no one referred to their religion. One knew they were Mohammedans—no need to work one's self up into a new frenzy about it every day. The problem here was the Turkish *power* —a most impressive power, it seemed.

Miguel listened with astonishment to genuine expressions of mourning when the Turkish Sultan, Suleiman, died. These men in Rome were actually grieving at the passing of a heathen!

Still listening, still observing, the reason for this became clearer. This Sultan who had died had been, it seemed, a monarch of great proportions, a man who belonged to the Occident as much as to the

Orient. He had been a protector of the arts, a man of wisdom, and even though he was a conqueror, at heart he had been a man of peace.

Obviously the same could not be said for his successor, Selim II. Descriptions of him went quickly around the Vatican City. "A drunkard," men said. "A swashbuckler . . . A braggart." This was a man who could easily do some foolish thing that would threaten all of Christendom.

Now Miguel began to understand the Roman view of a united world more clearly. It *was* a little absurd for Spain to be fighting the Protestants in the Netherlands; it was absurd of himself to be shocked when the Protestant Prince Elector of a German state was treated with as much reverence as a good Catholic prince from France. The unity of the Christian world as a whole was far more important than fighting between Protestants and Catholics in half a dozen countries.

For now, without any warning, and without any provocation, the new Sultan *did* do the foolish and incredible thing which everyone had feared.

Miguel was with the Monsignore when the messenger came with the news. "Selim has attacked and conquered the island of Cyprus." Miguel saw the young churchman stiffen. The papers he had been signing fell from his hands. "*Cyprus?*" he echoed.

Yes, it was true. Nor was this all. Selim had massacred the Christian population of the island and taken as hostages members of all the leading families.

The news ran through the Vatican like wildfire, then on through Rome and across the country. And then, while that news—the Turks on Cyprus, an Italian island which had belonged to Venice for years —was still being absorbed in all its horrifying implications, there came still more news. The hostages that Selim had taken, though all conditions for their release had been fulfilled, had been killed by the bloodthirsty Sultan, and their heads planted on the gates of the city.

The shock echoed through all of Europe—a Europe not particularly noted for sensitivity toward humanity. Both Christian and Turk, through continuous warfare, had grown used to brutality. But there were certain conventions even so; there were laws of war, and there was honor. The killing of the hostages was too much—and all Italy united in protest.

Monsignore Aquaviva shook his head. "This shows the kind of fool this Sultan is," he said. "With one stroke he has achieved what centuries of mediation could not accomplish—uniting the nations of Italy, indeed of Europe."

It was a miracle of a sorts, for the Italy of that day was far from the nation she is now. She was divided into many competing states, many of them under Spanish rule. Spain owned the southern end of the Italian Peninsula, along with the islands of Sicily and Sardinia. She held territories in the north, too. In the center of the Italian boot were the Papal States. In the north and northwest was the territory of Venice. Then, wedged in between these states, with their constantly changing frontiers, were several city states like Parma, Modena, Ferrara and others, vying with one another and waging small local wars for almost any reason under the sun.

Not one of these variously competing and warring states had the slightest reason to be sorry Venice had lost her possession, the island of Cyprus. Proud, rich Venice, built like a fairy-tale city right in the sea, filled with merchant spoils from all over the world—she could afford to lose an island.

But the outrage to human rights united them all. It did not matter to whom Cyprus had belonged. They thought of the Christians who had been massacred, the Christian hostages for whom ransom had been paid, who had been killed nonetheless. The states of Italy, the nations of Europe, were ready to unite in the name of common humanity. Their collective aim was to punish the aggressor.

The only difficulty was that, with all their fever for action, with all

their brawling, warlike background, not one of the little Italian states
had a proper army. Their own constant local wars were fought by
paid soldiers, who came and went with the jobs. Venice, that delicate, sea-going city, had never had an army. When she fought now
and then with her great merchant rival, Genoa, she fought at sea.
Even the big Papal state boasted only a few colorfully dressed Swiss
guards. The Pope was used to fighting with Papal bulls—very terrifying manifestoes to Christians—but for the Turks one needed bullets,
not bulls.

So now Miguel was witness to a new irony, and one day Monsignore Aquaviva asked him why he wore such a curious smile. "Your
pardon, Sire," answered Miguel. "I am afraid I am showing my
colors as a Spaniard. For so long I have heard Spain ridiculed for
her army, for always being so ready to fight. But now, for the same
reason, she is prized and courted."

Monsignore Aquaviva smiled too, a wry smile. It was true—hu-
miliating, but true. The Italians had to have Spanish help. There
was no other organized army but Spain's, no other ruler but the
King of Spain who could make this campaign a success. So there was
nothing for the Italians to do but put aside their pride and beg for
help.

And in such a cause the King of Spain was gracious, of course—
for a price. So, with Spanish cooperation, a crusade was now proclaimed and a union formed. It was given the name of the Holy

League, and each of the participating states contributed to it in ships and men—in proportion, as much as they could.

The idea of a crusade and the new name put this war above any local feuds. The aim was not one of terrestrial conquest; it was perhaps in the nature of a symbol. Not Spain, Venice and Genoa were fighting the Turks, but the Spirit of Christ. It ought not to be a war, but rather a demonstration, with military means.

With the crusade in preparation, and all Rome in a ferment of military talk, it was no longer possible for Miguel to go on as he had been, writing out letters for Monsignore Aquaviva, carrying messages back and forth. He had smiled when the Italians changed their tune about the Spanish army, but now all his own childhood dreams of being part of that army came hotly to his mind again. He too wanted to be part of the crusade, part of the host which carried the banners of God and the King against the Turk.

He went to his friend and protector, Aquaviva, and asked him for permission to enlist. The Monsignore granted it, a little reluctantly. "You have been a good assistant, Cervantes," he said. Then he looked at Miguel thoughtfully. "You should make a good soldier also. You have courage, intelligence—a calm head. But a soldier needs luck as well. With luck, you should make a very good soldier."

So Miguel packed up his few belongings and left Rome for Naples where the Spanish regiments were forming, a brand-new eagerness and excitement churning in his blood. He had known for a long time that he was not cut out for secretarial work. He believed now that the army was what he had always wanted. Before this time of crisis,

it would have been folly to enlist. The Spanish army needed soldiers, but of officers it had enough, so it was almost a rule that no two sons of a noble family could become officers. As Rodrigo already had his commission, Miguel would have had no luck in this direction. In the present emergency, however, surely this would all be changed. He too could become an officer.

He thought back on Aquaviva's words as he traveled to Naples. "You should make a good soldier. You have courage, intelligence, a calm head." It was true, these qualifications could lift a man high in a short time. There were many generals under thirty years of age. Perhaps he too . . . *but a soldier needs luck as well.* "Let me be lucky," Miguel whispered to himself. He began to foresee possibilities for himself which would never be his in any profession but soldiering.

And then he arrived in Naples, presented his letters of recommendation to the proper authorities—and was refused! It was too much to believe. The reason given was that he had first to offer documents which proved his pure Christian blood. This could be done, surely—but it took time, endless time. The Spanish army was very strict. A man had to prove unquestionably that he had not a drop of Moorish or Jewish blood in his veins; otherwise he had no chance of becoming an officer. Such a proof obviously would make a lengthy book, an extremely detailed document. It had to list the names of each of the eight great-grandparents, and follow the male members of the families even further—to the times of the Visigoths—and all the way to Noah! Yes, every Spaniard of some standing solemnly proved that one of his ancestors was descended from Noah.

In due time, after agonies of impatient waiting on Miguel's part, a document which proved he was related to Noah was achieved. Meanwhile, the preparations for the war had been hastened and were increasing in scale. More men and officers were needed than anticipated. Now, when Miguel handed over his lengthy proof of Christian blood, he was quickly accepted into the army without further question.

He was assigned to the regiment of Captain Mendoza, there to start his service as an ensign.

5

IN WHICH *Miguel takes part in a great naval battle, and receives a grave wound!*

ALL HIS LIFE long, Don Miguel de Cervantes had two loves—the theater and soldiering. The first he had discovered when he was a wide-eyed little boy of seven, watching the puppets at his first kermess. Forever after, the theater was to seem to him the truest reflection of nature—a symbol of life itself, wherein every man must choose his part and play it, giving meaning to his life through his dedication to his role. When, in his fifties, Cervantes sat in the Madrid jail, summoning the "Ingenious Knight, Don Quixote," out of the depths of his life and experience, he made this gray, lean man the greatest play-actor ever—a gentleman farmer, acting out in every fibre of his being the fancy that he is a knight.

Choosing the role was the thing that counted, and for Don Miguel, as for his knight, Don Quixote, soldiering was by far the bravest choice of all.

Miguel was twenty-four when he began his career as a soldier. Life, which had slowed to a crawl while he waited for his papers, suddenly speeded up to a quickstep as the army went to work trans-

forming civilians into fighting men.

The weeks in Naples went by swiftly, filled with trooping the colors, forming cadres, marching in big formations, or just standing in the sun for hours. When the pattern of his new life began to be less a blur, Miguel could see what a large military organization was being created for the crusade against the Turks. There were regiments composed of Spaniards, as his was; regiments of Italians, of Swiss and German mercenaries, and a smattering of all nationals. But for all the babel of tongues, soldiers of every nation shared a common language in swearing, fist-fighting, drinking and gambling.

Before very long the day arrived when the troops were shipped from Naples to Messina in Sicily, where all the members of the Holy League were foregathering. Miguel went aboard a Spanish galley called *The Marquesa,* on which he was to serve as an ensign under the command of General Figueroa, an experienced soldier of many campaigns.

When *The Marquesa* sailed into the Bay of Messina, Miguel saw that there were already more than two hundred ships riding at anchor there, a brave and heartening sight indeed. Their shipyards were full of men who overhauled the rigging and sails. Everywhere

sailors nailed, tarred, cleaned or repaired, but actually, in the main, the fleet was ready to sail. Everything waited on just one thing—the arrival of the supreme commander.

It had been difficult to find a man for this post, a man who would be acceptable to all the nations concerned. A Genoese would have been an insult to a Venetian; the republics of Venice and Genoa had been at war for centuries. A Roman would hardly have been acceptable to the Spaniards; a Spaniard would not be likely to please the Italians, who felt that there were too many Spaniards in Italy already. So finally, after much indecision, the choice had fallen on Don Juan of Austria—a half brother to the King of Spain, but still no Spaniard for all of that. Don Juan, in fact, belonged to none of the warring nations, nor had he any interest in the crusade other than the satisfaction of his vanity.

57

He and Philip of Spain were both sons of Charles V, a Hapsburg, Emperor of the Holy Roman Empire and also King of Spain. Don Juan, however, was illegitimate, the son of a mother with no royal blood, and hence heir to no kingdoms. He was twenty years younger than Philip, and what was even more irksome, under the tutelage of his royal brother.

The half brothers could hardly have been more different in temperament and inclinations, and they disliked each other heartily. Philip was a scholar by nature, a pedant and a perfectionist. It could happen that while his desk was loaded with documents requiring immediate attention, the King would lose a day correcting faulty Latin and scribbling sarcastic comments in the margins.

Don Juan ridiculed such idiosyncrasies, and himself having little in the way of mental capacities, proclaimed himself a man of action. The King had the nickname, *El Prudente*—The Cautious. Don Juan did everything to earn the name of The Daredevil.

His big opportunity to win this name had come a few years before the days of the Crusade, when he was chosen to put down a mutiny among the Moriscos of Spain. The Moriscos were those Moors or Arabs who had lived in Spain for centuries and had accepted the Christian faith. However, because they had kept their costumes and ways of life as of old, the government suspected that their faith was merely a matter of lip service and that actually they remained Mohammedans. As a result, the poor Moriscos were constantly under

government scrutiny, with soldiers popping into their homes at any time, to lift the lids on their pots to see if they were cooking pork, a meat Mohammedans refused to touch.

When a few Moriscos rebelled against this and other invasions of their privacy, and denied Spanish soldiers the right to enter their houses, the government decided on a punitive expedition. Don Juan was given command of this venture, and he sailed into it with a promise to spare nobody.

He kept his promise, too—turning the punitive expedition into a massacre. He emerged, steeped in blood, with the titles, Hero of Granada and Defender of the Faith.

This was the man who had been chosen supreme commander of the united fleet, the man on whom all the ships waited in the Bay of Messina. Meanwhile, the Hero of Granada tarried in Genoa as the guest of the city, making the most of a long round of festivities. Unmarried and a hero, he was drunk on the admiration of foolish young men and fawning young ladies, and seemed almost to have forgotten the reason he was in Italy.

On board *The Marquesa*, as it idly rode the gentle swells on the Bay of Messina, Miguel leaned on the rail and gazed at the great fleet of ships at anchor. It was the mightiest fleet ever assembled, so everyone said, and Miguel could well believe it. There were three hundred ships at least, mostly speedy galleys, but also bulky Spanish galleons, clumsy and hard to maneuver, but impressive looking because of their many decks. The great majority of the ships were Spanish, but the Venetians had added a respectable number, and so had the Genoese. The smallest group was composed of the Papal ships, an expression of good will rather than fighting power.

The ships' crews and the soldiers of this united fleet totalled seventy thousand men. Among them were many with some special training: cross-bow men from Switzerland, musketeers from Germany, gunners from France and Spain, and a great number of battle-hardened bowmen from many places in Europe.

"If only we could get started!" was Miguel's one thought; and it was the same for almost every one of the seventy thousand. They were bored to death with dice and cards and grumbling and waiting. Waiting—for the Hero of Granada.

Finally, at the very end of September, Don Juan managed to tear himself from the joys of Genoa. He arrived in Messina, went aboard his ship—and at last the fleet weighed anchor.

Slowly, the ships sailed across the Adriatic Sea toward the Dalmatian coast. For several days they cruised up and down between the many islands, until informers reported that the Turkish fleet, which had mustered nearly as many ships as the Holy League, had withdrawn deep into the Gulf of Corinth, the narrows splitting the Balkan Peninsula in two. The Turks, to all appearances, were trying to avoid battle at this particular time, for to follow them into such a trap seemed foolhardy.

Don Juan, however, was "The Daredevil." He came up with a plan to seal off the Turks in their own trap, banking on the fact that they could only retreat into narrower and narrower waters, whereas the Christian fleet was free to move back into the open sea if need be. So he gave orders to sail into the Gulf and make contact with the enemy.

LEPANTO

Very early in the morning of the seventh of October, some Greek shepherds gazed out onto the waters of the Gulf and beheld a sight that took their breaths away. They thought they were dreaming. At the narrowest part of the Gulf, where it is only two miles wide, next to the little fortress of Lepanto they saw two immense fleets—to the west, the ships of the Holy League, and to the east, in a wide circle, those of the Turks.

The shepherds were joined by peasants and farmers from round-about, but no matter how the gathering grew, the silence and the wonder held. Now, as the sun rose higher, the awed spectators saw the banners on the ships—crosses on the banners of the Genoese, the winged lion on the Venetian flag, the arms on the Spanish ships, and the crossed keys of the Papal fleet. On the other side, they could see the half-moon over the castles, the horse-tail ensigns, and the green flags of the Turks. The sun blazed on the sails of the Christian ships, big sails in dazzling colors, ornate with proud coats of arms. But in spite of all this brilliant display, a great silence reigned over the entire fleet.

Then, dreamlike in the silence, the ships of the Christian fleet began to move. Faintly, the men on the shore heard the far-off creak of oars, the splash of water as an oar rippled its surface. The sun rose higher, and they could see it flashing on the helmets and breast-plates of the men who packed the decks of the silent, moving ships.

Suddenly, the trance-like scene exploded into action. Sails flew downward and disappeared, furled along their yardarms. A number of galleys dashed forward in a crazy race, their guns spitting fire. The heavy cannon balls churned up the water, but did no harm as yet. The ships were still too far apart. But every second they drew closer, more guns were fired, and not all of the shots fell short.

And where was Miguel now, in this moment of moments, as the two fleets prepared to clash? Was the sun flashing off his helmet and breastplate, throwing its own small dazzle into the eyes on shore? Was Miguel now bending to a cannon, his heart high with excitement, his thoughts steady and calm and clear as the time for action drew near?

Alas, Miguel was no part of the scene at all, and the sudden, forward movement of his own ship came through to him as an almost meaningless swaying that simply enforced the dizziness that throbbed through his whole body. For Miguel was lying below deck in *The Marquesa*, stretched out in his bunk, stricken with fever. His bones ached, his stomach retched, he was alternately swept with waves of heat and icy chills. Somewhere, deep in his consciousness, he knew this was the day, the very hour, for which he had waited, and he groaned helplessly.

On the shore, the shepherds and the peasants caught their breaths and stood tensely, for now the battle was truly joined. Cannon balls were tearing holes in the sides of Turkish galleys, ripping shrouds and stays from the masts. Now there were shouts and cries

from the men on the ships. Whenever a shot found its mark, fierce shouts of jubilation went up from the Christian ships. *"Por Deos y Jesus!"* *"Avanti per la gloria della Madonna!"* Then the rumble of the next salvo would drown out the shouts, and a new sheet of thick, black smoke would rise to settle over the ships and the water.

Below deck, Miguel felt *The Marquesa* suddenly rock and shudder as its cannons fired. The shock ran through his body and he tried to rise from his bunk. The fight had begun! He *had* to get up and join his fellows. He heard the thud of running footsteps on the deck above, the shouts of his companions. "I'm coming! I'm coming!" he croaked. And then a new wave of dizziness seized him and he fell back, helplessly.

Out on the shore, the shepherds and the peasants moved their heads back and forth numbly. The Turkish ships were hardly idle as the Christians attacked. Shots were blazing from the east towards the Christian ships, and shouts of *"Allah il Allah!"* rose hoarsely in every pause between salvos.

Now ships were breaking loose from their squadrons, heavy gal-

leons were pressing into the enemy lines, vessels drew abreast of each other. On shore, the watchers heard the furious sound of breaking wood, the splitting of planks, the crack of breaking oars. There were clashing sounds as well—the whirr of axes and grappling irons and the clash of swords, as boarding parties leaped from Christian ship to Turkish, or vice versa.

Deep in the heart of *The Marquesa*, deep in the nightmare of heat and cold which enclosed Miguel, new shocks, new sounds intruded. The whole vessel shuddered; and then, with sudden clarity, Miguel heard, almost felt, the crunch of a grappling iron biting into the side of the ship. He heard a wild thudding of feet, cries, and shouted orders. With this new clarity of his brain, the truth burst in on him. *His* ship was being boarded! The Turks actually were on board *The Marquesa!*

Miguel clapped on his helmet without knowing how he did it. He half fell from his bunk, reached for his sword, and then, lacking armor or belt, naked sword in hand, he stumbled and ran, panting his way up the ladder to the deck.

Plunging out on the deck, the nightmare of his fever merged with the nightmare of reality. The deck swarmed with fighting men, his fellows and the heathen Turks in furious hand-to-hand struggles. Smoke billowed across them, its fumes choking Miguel's lungs. Then, above the savage shouts and curses of the Turks, he heard a voice he knew. "Take twelve men, set out in the pinnace, and smash their accursed grappling irons!"

Swaying, blinking, Miguel looked about for men he could summon to join him so that he could carry out the command. "Hernando!" he cried hoarsely. Then, even as he spied another familiar figure and started to cry his name, a flash of burning pain suddenly rocked him, spinning him around.

Coming out of the first shock, he clutched his arm, looked down and saw his hand, a mass of bloody pulp. He clenched his teeth. It would not stop him, even so. "Juan!" he cried. Then a second bolt struck him, and he plunged, senseless, to the deck.

Unconscious, then, Miguel lay there as his shipmates ran around and over him, hurrying desperately to carry out the captain's order. Senseless he continued to lie, as the hand-to-hand struggles raged over him and the Turks gave ground—slowly, almost imperceptibly at first, but steadily at last. Senseless he still lay, when, panting and bloody, his fellows cheered the last Turk falling over the side of *The Marquesa*.

On the shore, the watchers still stood frozen to the spot, unable or unwilling to speak a word. They knew a decisive battle was being fought, even though they themselves were not for either side. Now they gazed through the great pall of smoke as one ship after another took fire, flaming like a giant torch. They saw tiny figures leaping from the ships into the sea, weighed down by irons and armor—hundreds of such leaping, disappearing figures, human beings all of them—but there was nothing the watchers could do but gasp and press their knuckles to their mouths. They saw the struggles continue in the water—a soldier climbing onto a broken mast, another soldier reaching up from the water, plunging the dagger in his hand into the first soldier's back. They saw drowning men choking one another with their bare hands and biting one another like wild beasts. Would there never be an end to it?

Then, finally, they saw that the end was coming. The Turkish fleet, so brave and strong that morning at dawn, was a ragged remnant now. One Turkish ship after another floated past, ablaze from her waterline to the tip of her masts. Some went by all aglow, tarrying a while before sinking from sight. Others plummeted to the bottom as if by some swift decision. Still others slowly drifted to shore, there to keel over on their sides.

At last there was quiet again. The shadows of evening moved over the Gulf of Corinth, and the shepherds and peasants took one

last look, sighed deep sighs, and went towards their homes, then paths lighted fitfully by the reflections of the fires that still burned out on the water.

The Battle of Lepanto was over and the Turks were vanquished with a thoroughness of which no one had really dared to dream.

On the Spanish ships, men stood in the stench of blood and smoke and, without an order, doffed their helmets and sank to their knees. Softly at first, then ever more loudly, a *Te Deum* poured from thousands of throats. It rang out over the water, filled the coastal valleys, and reverberated back from all the surrounding mountains— a song of thanks to God.

Below deck once more, in the hatch with the other wounded men, Miguel heard a dim echo of the song, but it had no meaning for him. It would be many, many days before anything but pain had meaning.

That night, and the next day and the next, bonfires on many mountaintops signalled news of the victory, and as the news began to spread through the Western world, bells pealed in town after town, men and women knelt in thanksgiving, and there were solemn processions in all the cities of Italy and Spain.

But night and day were all one in the sick bay where Miguel lay, every breath seeming to tear something in his chest, on which lay the bloody stump which had been his hand. Around him there were endless moans and prayers and sobs, punctuated now and then with a scream of pain or delirium. As consciousness began to come back, at first fitfully, Miguel was aware of the figure of a monk moving about in the dimness, bending over the prostrate forms of the men. Slowly, painfully, Miguel's mind worked out the significance of the monk's presence; and when finally the man bent over him, he whispered, "We have won?"

"Yes, my son," answered the monk, softly. "With God's help we have won a glorious victory. Now let me see how I can help you. Let me see how your wound is dressed."

A glorious victory! Miguel closed his eyes, satisfied. It would be long before he knew or understood that glorious as the victory had been, the Turks were scarcely destroyed by this one defeat at sea.

Basically, the Turks were a nation of horsemen. As horsemen they had acquired a vast territory in sparsely settled country. With brilliant cavalry maneuvers they had conquered Hungary, and had even approached Vienna. They had spread their realm in Africa and disputed the coast from Egypt to Morocco. They had gone conquesting in the East till India's multitudes checked them. Everywhere horses could go they went. But in naval action they were inexperienced, and so at Lepanto they were defeated.

It was a blow, of course, and it taught the Turks a good lesson—that the Christians could unite when need be. They had never quite believed this possible, but now they knew better.

But the defeat at sea lost them none of their territory. Later, much later, Miguel learned with consternation and almost disbelief, that for all the drubbing they had taken, the Turks still held the island of Cyprus, the capture of which had touched off the battle. Could it really be true? All Christendom had armed, and had gone in pursuit of the Turks—because they had taken Cyprus. All Christendom had fallen on the Turks and punished them for the deed. And then, after the punishment, there they were, still holding Cyprus. All through Miguel's life they held it, and for hundreds of years after, until it was finally purchased by England. It was an irony that Miguel could

not fail to appreciate in later years—a glorious victory that totally failed in one of its prime aims.

But now, lying in the sick bay, all this knowledge lay ahead of him, in the future. Gradually, as sense and understanding returned, Miguel picked up other facts from the monk during the holy man's daily visits. He learned that though the Turks had lost most of their ships, the Spanish-Italian fleet was in bad shape too. The ships were afloat, but that was about all. Very few had their sails; many were burned almost to the waterline. Others lacked masts, and almost all had lost their oars and rudders. Nor was this the only price of victory. Thousands had been slain and many thousands more lay wounded in ships' bunks and sick bays, even as Miguel. It would be weeks before the fleet could leave for home.

These were dreadful weeks in the sick bay of *The Marquesa*, filled as it was with over a hundred wounded men, crammed into a space large enough for only thirty. The stench of blood and festering wounds combined with the stifling heat to make nights and days an endless agony. Most of the time Miguel lay in a sort of stupor, his left hand lying upon him like a strange limb, and his chest constantly torn with pain.

Finally, on the twentieth day after the battle, Miguel heard the creak of beams and felt the ship roll. His heart lifted a little as he realized they must be headed out to sea—headed towards home. With a smile he dozed off into real slumber.

In Messina the barracks and the hospital tents were quickly overcrowded, but at least here it was bright and clean, almost a paradise compared to the ship. When Miguel was examined at the hospital, the wounds in his chest which had caused him such torment were found to be painful but hardly dangerous. They had been caused by one fractured rib which was mending now. His hand, however, was in far worse shape. Nothing could be done about it. Only because of his general good health had he escaped gangrene. "Suppose your hand is useless," the doctors told him. "You're lucky you still have it." So that was that.

Miguel remained in the hospital till his rib was completely healed, and it was not until six months after the battle that he reported back to his regiment. While in the hospital, he was promoted and decorated, and when he returned to military service Don Miguel de Cervantes was a lieutenant.

6

WHICH TELLS *how Don Miguel languished in a garrison, met his long-lost brother, and then won hope of promotion!*

AWAY WITH those who would tell you that letters have the **advantage** over arms!" said the gentleman-knight, Don Quixote, **years** later. Of course, as you have heard, that fellow was not in full possession of his wits. He was mad on the subject of chivalry. However, on every other subject under the sun he spoke so rationally and so winningly, he left his listeners quite bemused. One thing seems fairly sure: Don Quixote spoke for his author, Don Miguel, when he spoke of the glory of soldiering.

It was hard to have a useless left hand, to be virtually one-handed at the age of twenty-five. But Miguel bore his handicap proudly. "The scars that a soldier has to show . . . are stars that guide others to the Heaven of honor," he said.

It was difficult, too, to be suddenly thrust into garrison life with all its tedium, after such a brief burst of action at Lepanto. But Miguel would not complain about that either.

The regiment was stationed in a somber old castle in Naples, a dark and ancient pile of stone which had not been remodelled since the days of the Normans three hundred years before. The rooms were dank, the interior a maze of stairs, corridors and vaults.

As for his fellow soldiers, they were a rather trying lot, away from the challenge and comradeship of battle. The officers were mostly young men, younger than Miguel. All of them were cocky, boisterous fellows, bored with garrison life, but with no sensible ideas at all about how to fill their idle hours. As a result, anything that promised a diversion was welcome.

Miguel watched with dismay as they formed gangs and roamed the countryside, harassing the farmers, ransacking houses, looting and pillaging—all in the gay, carefree spirit of youngsters who were

simply having fun. Individually, not one of the men was really bad, but joined together, a wild spirit of malicious mischief seemed to infect them all.

They would hang a farmer from a tree on a bet that the branch would not hold. They would slice a man to show how sharp their sword was. They were always hungry, since the food in the mess consisted mainly of chickpeas, day in and day out. Being hungry, they foraged everywhere. If they found a hen or a piglet, a jar of honey or a ham in some poor farmer's larder, they grabbed it with a shout. When the farmer protested, he was simply kicked head forward into the barnyard manure.

At other times they looked for provisions at the monasteries. The monks cursed them in Latin, Italian and Spanish, but this did not

protect a monastery's stocks of wine or its precious bacons and hams.

And of course, along with hunting for food, there were always pretty girls to pursue. It often happened that two groups of soldiers, one Spanish, the other German or Swiss, were after the same local damsel. This game gave the men a wonderful excuse to do battle over a maiden in distress. The Spaniards were haughty and conceited to a degree that was painful, but the Germans, in their turn, were coarse and swashbuckling. Their fantastic dress, in blatant colors, with ribbons and feathers all over, was a provocation in it-

self. Every Spaniard felt the urge to rip the German clothing, to drag the German feathers in the mud.

But all the men were good swordsmen, trained to kill, so these skirmishes often became quite serious. In such cases, the colonel in command could not look away, as he did when food was pilfered. He had to order that the culprit who started the fight, if still alive, run the gauntlet, or be flogged. The whip was hard, the executioner was strong—sometimes the punishment was fatal. Still, next day the same games started anew. What else was there to do?

For Miguel, there had to be something else. In his idle hours he went to the monasteries, which his comrades had raided for food, to borrow books—and found, as long ago on the road, that there was

good conversation to be had with the monks who lived there. But being Miguel, he did not confine his conversation to these men. He spoke with everyone he met as he walked along. He talked with the peasants about their harvests, played with the children, chatted with the innkeeper, and often helped the innkeeper's wife with a heavy basket of wet laundry.

If Miguel watched the pranks of his fellows with dismay, they looked on his activities with equal alarm. Could he really be a nobleman and consort so amiably with mere peasants? Surely there must be something in the rules that forbade an officer to fraternize with everyone as did this Cervantes. Still, when it came to a point, they could not snub him.

Every morning at the garrison there was fencing practice. Because of his useless hand, Miguel had to practice especially hard, and soon he cut such a fine figure on the fencing ground that no one could doubt his nobility.

Then, gradually, he began to be accepted, reluctantly admired even, because of his other differences. Because he kept himself apart from the hotheads of the regiment and was never involved in quarrels himself, he was often asked to mediate when an argument threatened to become serious. From the role of mediator, he went on to being almost a father confessor to some of the officers. All the long-ago years on the road, when he had listened, asked questions and listened again, had made him a man to whom others instinctively turned when they wanted to talk about themselves.

Most of the men had the same problems: debts, duels, love affairs. And most of the problems would have been easy enough to settle by means of a frank explanation or an apology. But the fierce Spanish pride of most made it almost impossible to admit personal blame. Only to Miguel would they confess it. Then they would listen uneasily when he asked them if it was really so impossible to apologize. Quietly, earnestly, without any pomposity, Miguel managed to con-

vince some of these comrades that it would not do damage to their
honor to follow such a simple course; in fact, it might even increase
it. Gradually Miguel began to acquire quite a "clientele." Even the
older officers came to him with their troubles. *Mano,* the "One-
Armed," was what they called him now, and Miguel answered to
the name with pride. "The scars a soldier bears are stars . . ."

So the months went by at the garrison, to become years. And
Miguel began to be wildly restive. This was not soldiering, this endless monotony of life in a garrison. At the end of the first year, some
of the officers who had arrived with Miguel left to take up fighting as-
signments. Miguel hurried to the colonel to ask why he too had not
been chosen for combat duty. Was it his useless hand? The colonel
reassured him: his time would come. But another year passed; more
of his fellows left the garrison. A new crop of lieutenants arrived, and
Miguel again went to the colonel. When was his time coming?
Patience, the colonel counseled. And so yet another year went by.

In his restlessness and misery during this time, Miguel found only
one solace—the poetry that he had attempted to write once before,
in Madrid. Now, when it seemed he could not stand the garrison a
moment longer, when it seemed he must shout and run amok from
sheer boredom, he would retire to some place where no one could
disturb him. There, alone with a scrap of paper, a quill pen and
some ink, he would sit down to compose a poem. Thus, for a little
while, the walls of the garrison and the irritations inside them faded
away. For a little while he would be out in a wide and shining world
where great deeds were performed, great songs sung.

But the moments of escape never could last long. Military life makes sure no man has much time for private thought or reflection. Military life is life lived in the company of others. So the endless days continued to pass, till Miguel began to feel as though he were a piece of furniture in the garrison—a lieutenant who had been there always.

He stood on the ramparts of the old castle one evening and watched the sun set beyond the harbor of Naples—just as he had watched it so many hundreds of times. He looked across the harbor to the twin peaks of Mount Vesuvio, and he looked at them with loathing, because they had become so graven on his mind. He gazed at the ships in the harbor and it seemed he knew them all—knew the schedules of their comings and goings, knew the very passengers who came and went through the years.

Was this the end of the road for him? Miguel asked himself. Was he doomed to rust away, to decay here, rooted always to this one spot—and after a life that always before had been filled with wandering? Why, only five years ago he had been in Rome—at least an observer of men and activities of importance. Now here he stood.

That night he went to bed in despair—and woke next morning to the surprise of his life! A visitor was waiting for him in the main hall, a visitor at whom Miguel stared, unbelieving, as the man walked towards him. There was something about that solid, burly figure, that round and rock-like head, which roused old memories. Miguel began to run, and the visitor ran too. The two men fell into each other's arms.

It *was* Rodrigo, the big brother who had vanished from his life— how long ago now? Fifteen years at least! A surge of love for this

childhood companion brought tears to Miguel's eyes. Rodrigo, the unemotional, was almost as much affected.

There were greetings and hasty explanations on both sides, and then Rodrigo began to look about. He was a hardened soldier now, toughened by many campaigns, and he needed no more than a glance to see how things were at this garrison in Naples, how little they promised for Miguel.

"Man alive, brother!" he cried. "How long did you say you've been here?"

"Almost five years," Miguel answered. "Each year the colonel promises that next year I'll be assigned somewhere else, or get a promotion."

"A promotion—*here?*" Rodrigo's voice held scorn. "Would you think to find bacon where there are no pigs? Does a bee in the desert make honey? Who looks for wine in an empty skin! In other words, brother, you'll get nothing here—but older!"

Miguel was laughing in spite of himself at Rodrigo's wild string of proverbs. But he knew that what his brother said was true. There was no hope for him so long as he stayed at this forlorn outpost.

"A man with a journey to make starts walking," Rodrigo continued. "Better still, a man with a journey to make gets a horse. Get a horse, brother. Get a letter from someone above the rank of this stupid colonel of yours. Who is the regiment's commanding officer, by the way—and has he anything against you?"

"He is General Figueroa," answered Miguel. "I served under him at Lepanto, and, as far as I know, he likes me well. He commended me for bravery in action there."

"Good, good. We'll get a letter from him. But wait—Lepanto? You served at Lepanto?"

"Of course. That was where my hand was shattered."

"Lepanto. Don Juan of Austria was Supreme Commander there against the Turks."

"That is right," Miguel agreed.

"Brother of mine," cried Rodrigo, "what sort of soldier are you? You sit in a cell when the doors are open. You die of thirst in the middle of a rainstorm. You served in Don Juan's army, he was your personal supreme commander! *He* will give you a letter to the King himself, and with that sort of a recommendation, you can get any sort of post you choose."

"Is it possible?" Miguel sounded incredulous.

"Is it possible!" Rodrigo exploded now. "Can a dog scratch fleas? Can a gentle maiden bring a strong man to his knees? Can—?"

"All right, all right!" laughed Miguel. "It is possible." He was unbelievably heartened by his brother's enthusiasm and his hard common sense.

"Of course you will need a letter of introduction from the General to Don Juan, but if the General thinks well of you, that will only be a formality. Come! How quickly can you get a furlough?"

The furlough, it developed, would not take long to arrange. In just a few days the brothers sailed off to Messina, where General Figueroa was stationed.

Figueroa received them kindly. He remembered Don Miguel quite well. He would be glad indeed if he could help arrange a better assignment for the Lieutenant. However, there was no use not being frank. The disabled hand did make the Lieutenant more or less unfit for active service.

Hearing this, Miguel's face so plainly reflected his disappointment that the General cleared his throat and tried to sound more hopeful. At least he could promise that he personally would do everything in his power to obtain a captaincy for Miguel.

This was fine, of course, but now Rodrigo nodded at Miguel to remind him that the business was not yet finished. It was still necessary

83

to ask the General if he could obtain a letter of recommendation for
Miguel from Don Juan.

Miguel phrased the request as carefully and as diplomatically as
possible, but on hearing Don Juan's name the General's friendliness
chilled a bit. There was a moment or two of silence, and both
brothers felt their hopes fading. Obviously, the rumors that the General had no liking for Don Juan were true.

Suddenly the General made up his mind. He smiled at Miguel.
Such a letter would have great weight for the young man and it was
not as though he were currying favor for himself.

"Very well, Lieutenant," he said abruptly. "I shall see the Commander, and you will hear from me."

With many expressions of thanks the brothers withdrew, to wait
as patiently as possible for the outcome of the General's interview
with Don Juan.

Remembering Don Juan's arrogant behavior when the whole
Christian fleet had waited for him at Messina five years before, and
remembering many another tale he had heard of Don Juan's whims
and fancies, Miguel could not help being nervous.

Indeed, if he had known just how things were going for the General in his attempt to help him, Miguel would have turned pale with
alarm. The General had expected Don Juan to be disagreeable, but
he had not expected to be insulted. Insult was what he received,
however, when he finally managed to achieve an interview with the
famous man. General Figueroa handed the Don the letter of recommendation he had prepared for him to sign. Don Juan barely looked

84

at it, tossed it aside, and requested Figueroa to leave. Before the General could utter a word, the guards had opened the door and shown him out.

Burning with rage and resentment, General Figueroa was now determined that Don Juan should sign the letter. The next day he returned, insisted on being seen, and once again handed him the paper.

When Don Juan saw it was the same letter he had tossed aside the day before, it was his turn to fly into a rage. This time he threw the disputed paper to the floor and, without ceremony, ordered the General out.

Quietly, Figueroa picked up the letter, and, in the same movement, unsheathed his sword. The next moment he laid both sword and letter on the desk before Don Juan.

"Sire," he said, "either I receive your signature to this letter, or I retire from the service. What will happen thereafter is for my lord, the King, to decide."

There was a moment of quiet tension. Then Don Juan furiously took up his quill, signed the letter, and handed it to the General without a glance in his direction. Figueroa picked up his sword, bowed deeply, and left the room.

So it was that Miguel received the all-important recommendation from Don Juan, not actually becoming the cause of a mortal feud

between the General and the Commander, perhaps, but certainly the innocent cause of an open eruption of the hostility between these two men.

There was really no way to apologize to the General for this. Miguel thanked him earnestly for his efforts; that was all he could do.

One more letter was needed—a certificate of good conduct covering the period of Miguel's stay in Naples and Sicily. This was easy to obtain from his good friend, Don Carlos of Aragon, Duke of Sesea, the Viceroy of the Realm.

Now, with three letters to present to the King—three highly valuable documents—Rodrigo told Miguel that he was properly armed to return to Spain. As it happened, a flotilla was preparing to set sail for Spain almost immediately.

"Two heads are better than one," Rodrigo observed. "Where wine is being poured, anyone's cup may be filled. I will go with you, and —who knows?—I may step up a rank or two myself."

So Miguel bade farewell to all his comrades at the garrison in Naples, and together the two brothers embarked on the good ship *Sol*. It was September 25, 1575. After an absence of six years, Miguel was returning to Spain.

7

IN WHICH *our hero and his brother are captured by the Barbary pirates!*

THE SHORTEST way to travel between Naples in Italy and Valencia in Spain would have been to sail almost due west, through the Straits of Bonifacio, the narrows between the islands of Corsica and Sardinia. However, the captain of *The Sol,* like all mariners on the Mediterranean in those days, lived in healthy fear of the Barbary pirates. He preferred to go the long way around, following the coast line of Italy and France. Furthermore, he was pleased to have the company of two other ships, so they sailed in a convoy of three. At night the vessels either tried for a port, or anchored very close to shore.

It promised to be a long voyage, but a pleasant one. The weather was mild, the sea was calm, and for Miguel and Rodrigo, it was entertainment enough to lounge on deck and gaze shoreward at the many little towns, castles and watchtowers which dotted the land. They could see fishermen dragging in their nets, exchanging greetings with the washerwomen—who all seemed beautiful from this distance. Full of great plans for the future though the brothers were, this was a cheerful interlude.

The Sol had rounded the Cape of Antibes on the French coast and they were sailing slowly towards the Isles of Hyeres, not far from Toulon, when it happened.

Suddenly, all three ships were surrounded by a fleet of small, light ships—the Barbary pirates! They seemed to have come from nowhere. Hardly had the crews of *The Sol* and the other ships cried out in alarm, when the Berber ships were alongside. Then a host of armed and colorfully dressed men were swarming aboard.

It was useless to struggle, useless to try any form of violence. All the captain's precautions had been in vain after all. In an instant, all

three ships were captives of the Berbers.

Miguel and Rodrigo stood stunned, watching as the pirates coolly went about their business, almost like official customs inspectors. They disarmed the captain, the crew, and the passengers. Rodrigo and Miguel handed over their swords without a murmur, surrounded as they were by half a dozen impassive Berbers.

Then the pirates directed all their captives aboard the various Berber ships; pirates took the helms of *The Sol* and the other Italian ships. The pirate chieftain called out an order, and all the boats were swung about to head southward, towards Algeria.

As the voyage south got under way, the pirate chieftain himself began a thorough inspection of every prisoner and his belongings. Each man was examined as though he were a horse or a cow. His teeth were inspected and his muscles tested. Then his papers and his belongings were given careful scrutiny. Strong and healthy young men would bring a good price as slaves in Algiers. But if papers or other belongings indicated wealth or position, this meant that the man possessing them could be held for a fine ransom figure.

When it was Rodrigo's turn for inspection, the chieftain nodded approvingly at his sturdy build. He was not so young, this one, but he was tough and well-muscled. Then it was Miguel's turn, and the chieftain frowned, glancing at his maimed hand. With a hand like that, he would not be good for much as a slave. Still frowning, he went through Miguel's papers. And then he found the letters—the one signed by General Figueroa, the other letter bearing the signature of Don Juan of Austria—and addressed to no less a personage than the King of Spain. The chieftain's brows went up and Miguel heard him give a pleased whistle through his teeth.

Presently Miguel, Rodrigo and the rest of the captives on the ship were bound loosely together, and shoved down into the hold. The hatch was closed and the pirates were ready to forget about their prisoners till they landed in Algiers.

The air was fetid and it was horribly crowded in the hold. Soon a new misery was added: the ships were sailing close to the wind in a rolling ground swell, and every now and then water broke over the sides and poured into the hold, drenching everyone with brine. Soaked, miserable, and seasick to boot, the men endured the next

forty-eight hours as in a nightmare.

Now and then Miguel and Rodrigo would try to rally each other with encouraging words. One of them would whisper, "We'll escape somehow. People *do* escape. It happens all the time." "Of course," the other would agree. Secretly, though, both of them battled black despair. People *did* escape from the pirates, true, but it was not easy. And they had been so close to such a brave future.

At last the voyage was over, the hatch was lifted and the captives hauled out to blink in the blazing sun. Ashore, they saw the whitewashed walls and turrets of Algeria's capital city, Algiers, the great fortress of the Casbah on its height, looming over the clustered roofs below.

Briskly now, the captain of the pirate ship was dividing the cap-

tives into two groups, the strong and the weak. With a sinking heart, Miguel watched as Rodrigo was wrested from his side and pushed over among the strong; while he, with his useless hand, was left with the weak.

The strong were herded off the ship first, to be marched to the slave market. Rodrigo tried to turn, to wave back to his brother, but the pirate beside him yanked him on. Miguel raised his voice. "Be of good cheer, Rodrigo. We will get out of this somehow, and meet again. God be with you, brother." Then it was his turn to be drawn along with the others in his group, off the ship and out towards the market.

For once in his life, it was difficult for Miguel to gaze with interest at a new, strange scene. All around him were the bustle and excitement of a busy foreign city, the home base of the Barbary pirates, ruled for more than half a century by the Turks. But Miguel was blind to the color and glitter of the bazaars, the throngs of Berbers and Turks all around him going about their business. He was a

90

captive, **about to be sold into** slavery. Was there any way to break
loose, **to escape the fate ahead?** He kept his eyes on his **captors,**
waiting for a possible moment of inattention.

But there was none. Now they had arrived at the slave market. In
the center of the market was a small platform which was raised
above the crowd of buyers and onlookers. From the platform a
white-robed Berber was auctioning off a black man. Not far from
Miguel a solid-looking fellow, dressed in bright silks and wearing a
jeweled turban, raised his hand languidly, signalling his bid. Scattered here and there throughout the crowd were other evidences of
men of means; they all had the same casual but businesslike interest
in the proceedings.

Slavery here in North Africa, and all through the Near and **Far
East,** was such an old and taken-for-granted institution that no **one**
had any qualms about it at all. Men needed laborers for all sorts **of**
work. How better acquire them than by buying them? Here **in the**
Algiers market, slaves **were** brought in from many areas. **There were**

tribesmen from the interior of Africa, like the black man who had just been purchased. There were men and women from the East, and there were many Europeans, like Miguel and Rodrigo, who had been taken captive on the high seas.

Miguel's eyes were on the motley throng of prisoners as he looked everywhere for Rodrigo, but there was no sign of him. Then there was a tug on his chain, and it was his turn to be led up onto the platform, to be displayed to the prospective customers.

The auctioneer looked at Miguel's bad hand and frowned. Then the pirate who held his chain leaned forward, spoke a few rapid words and held up Miguel's letters. The auctioneer's attitude changed at once. Now he turned to the customers and began to harangue them eagerly. Not understanding a word, Miguel could sense that the auctioneer was brushing aside his handicap, referring extravagantly to the letters, and promising any prospective buyer that here was a man who might be worth a fortune in ransom money. Eerie as it felt to be standing there, nothing but a piece of merchandise, Miguel could not help being thankful that the letters and the maimed hand protected him from being bought as a galley slave. The hardships of such a fate would be almost beyond endurance.

Someone was bidding for Miguel. The bid was accepted. Now a fat Berber was wending his way to the platform, smiling a fat, greedy smile. He was after the letters. A few words, a clap of the hands, and one of the Berber's attendants took Miguel's chain, making it clear that he was to follow him.

So Miguel was purchased by Dali Mami, a rich Berber who made himself richer by dabbling in such human investments as Miguel. In a courtyard of his palace, he kept a whole group of unfortunate

captives while he awaited money for their ransom from friends or relatives abroad. These Miguel now joined.

It was a pleasant enough courtyard, at first glance—clean, and shadowed from the sun by graceful colonnades. All the men quartered there looked up eagerly as Miguel was thrust among them. They too were clean, and appeared well-fed. Some were playing games, others held flutes or guitars, but they put aside whatever they were doing to cluster around Miguel. What was his story? What were his hopes for a speedy ransom? This, of course, Miguel did not know yet, but the desperate eagerness of the men to make the most of his arrival made it very clear how tedious their own days of imprisonment were.

In a little while, Miguel was brought fresh clothes and a good meal. Then, when he was clean and fed, a guard came again to lead him before Dali Mami. This gentleman had obviously been studying Miguel's letters with great care and had reached very happy conclusions. Rubbing his hands, he told Miguel that he would immediately be given the materials with which to write his family in Spain. He was to request from them, as a price for his liberty, five hundred gold ducats!

Five hundred ducats! Miguel felt the tiled floor tilt a little beneath his feet. The whole cool, shadowed room seemed to rock. He had been wondering if his family could raise fifty or a hundred ducats, somehow, if they knew this was the amount required to save him. But five hundred!—why, that was more than most military officers earned in the course of a lifetime. It was a staggering sum. Even if his whole family sold everything but their barest necessities, and all his relatives and friends contributed whatever they could, they still would not be able to collect such a ransom.

In a daze, Miguel accepted writing materials from the guard. Back in the courtyard he sat in a state of numbness, trying to devise some way to compose a letter making this impossible request. His fellow captives, when they heard the sum demanded, shook their heads in sympathy. Finally, somehow, Miguel got his letter written. But now, for the first time since his capture, he felt completely demoralized. He could not see how in the world there could be the slightest chance of his ever being ransomed.

For a while, he simply sank into the routine of the life in the courtyard. He ate, he washed, he talked with the other captives. Gradually, of course, being Miguel de Cervantes, in spite of his own misery, he became interested in the stories of his fellow prisoners. One by one, he drew them out; he heard of their lives at home in France, or in Italy, or Spain—heard of their loves, their sorrows; how they had been captured, their hopes for the future. But then, as the days passed into weeks, even this interest was exhausted. Miguel knew every detail of each man's history and they of his. So the men sat brooding through the endless hours of the Algerian afternoons, each a little island of loneliness and despair.

Miguel sat in his own tiny circle of solitude and considered the irony of his fate. After five years of languishing in the tedium of the Naples garrison, the future had suddenly begun to bloom with the

promise of advancement, perhaps even action. Then almost immediately his capture had destroyed the promise. He was returned to a tedium even vaster and more hopeless than the one he had known in Naples before Rodrigo appeared. Rodrigo! There, at least, was *something* he could do. He could ask the guard once more if his friends outside the palace had found any clues as to Rodrigo's fate.

Talking to the guard at the gate to the courtyard served a double purpose: Miguel was doing what he could to relieve his anxiety about Rodrigo, and he was learning the Berber language too. Some day, somehow, this language might be of use.

Finally, after a number of months, Miguel received a letter from his mother. He opened it with shaking hands, wondering how on earth she had been able to respond to the news of her sons' capture, and the preposterous ransom request as well. Then, with a lifting of the heart, he saw that Doña Leonora had indeed responded like the noblewoman she was. She told him not to despair. She also promised that she and his father would take every possible step to raise the needed money. In the meantime, he must be patient and he must not lose hope.

Miguel closed his eyes as a wave of misery swept over him. It made him physically sick to think of his aging parents being put to this new trial: of his father, who must swallow his pride and stoop before persons of influence to ask for help, and of his sisters who would sacrifice the few little trinkets they possessed in the futile hope that they might help.

Somehow, though, his mother's letter jarred him from his apathy. Through the weeks in the courtyard, all the captives talked of escape. Now Miguel began to think of it seriously, and to apply all the weight of his intelligence to the problem. It was one thing to talk about escape, another thing entirely to carefully plan an attempt with the firm resolve of carrying it out. Failure, he knew, could mean death.

The first question he had to settle was whether or not he should make his attempt alone. Finally, since he felt there were more chances of success if several worked together, he decided to ask all the captives which of them wanted to take the gamble. Soon he had a devoted group of followers, ardently awaiting the hour, which he was to decide.

Although Miguel's preparations consisted almost entirely of winning the help of Dali Mami's secretary, through whom the prisoners sent and received their mail, it was many weeks before they could hope to attempt to make their break. First they needed provisions, sturdy boots, and directions as to the roads to take if they succeeded in fleeing Dali Mami's house. The secretary, a renegade Christian, was endangering his own life by helping them, and he moved with exceeding caution.

Finally, one moonless night, Miguel and five companions, weary of waiting any longer, bade a whispered farewell to the men who were staying behind, and climbed over the courtyard wall, using a rope ladder. Their plan was to travel as far as possible that night, hide during the next day, then travel on again the next night, hoping that they would somewhere find a Christian who would aid them in their flight.

It was not so vague a plan as it might sound. Most of the cities along the North African coast had a Christian quarter. Miguel hoped they would reach one such quarter, and remain hidden there until they could board a ship for Spain. Algiers, of course, had its Christian section, but the Christians there would not dare to harbor six fugitives from Algiers itself. In any of the other cities, however, they could pass for travelers. The plan of traveling by night had much to be said for it. The coolness would be refreshing. They would not suffer from thirst, and—most important of all—they were not likely to be seen.

This night was a particularly dark one, and even after the eyes of the escaping captives grew accustomed to the darkness, they still could see practically nothing. An orderly pace was out of the question. They tried to cling to each other, groping their way, tripping and stumbling, constantly halting because someone had tumbled into a ditch or lost his bearings. All the while they kept calling out each others' names in hoarse whispers to make sure they were all together.

Then dawn came—and they saw they were still within sight of the towers of Algiers. It was a blow to them all. They had hoped to cover at least ten miles the first night; they had gone less than two! Now, in order not to be seen, they crept behind a small mosque shrine in a Moslem cemetery.

As the day wore on, they had to huddle together in order to avoid the relentless sun. The air quivered in the intense heat. No one said a word. Miguel's mind, like the minds of all his companions, was very nearly a blank. He stared into the distance without seeing anything. Hardly aware of what it signified, he saw the men around him close their eyes and doze off, one by one. After an hour or so, overcome by the heat and the glitter, Miguel too slept.

It was thus, fast asleep, that Dali Mami's guards discovered them.
And so ended the attempted escape.

Going back to the palace, the guards prodding them along, all the
men felt chill in spite of the burning heat. It seemed there could not
be any doubt about what awaited them when they arrived before
Dali Mami—it would be death, in one form or another. Perhaps it
would be a gruesome death, carried out with the lingering attention
to detail for which the Berbers were famous; perhaps their heads
would simply be cut off, quickly and without ceremony. Either way,
not a man but was sure his capture spelled doom.

As he stumbled along, Miguel nourished one faint hope—the hope
that he might at least save his companions, who had made this attempt at his instigation. When the miserable group was finally
pushed before Dali Mami, Miguel stepped forward and began to
speak.

He spoke slowly, using as many Berber words as he could remember, and he asked that he alone be punished. He explained that

it was he, and he alone, who was responsible for this foolish act, and he implored Dali Mami to show mercy for his comrades. He spoke with his hands and entire body as well as with words. He acted out every role. He tried every trick he could think of.

Miguel finally finished, and Dali Mami sat impassive. There was a thick silence in the cool and shadowed hall where Dali Mami had received them. Miguel felt a ringing in his ears, and his heart seemed to pound all through his body.

Then Dali Mami gave an order. The guards seized the trembling Christians and led them through the long halls, until they found themselves again in the courtyard which they had left only the night before. They stood and stared at each other incredulously. All but one of the guards departed; this one simply locked the door, then took up his usual station beside it. *They were not going to be punished after all! No one was going to be punished.* And it was all Miguel's doing.

What was Miguel's secret? How was it this undistinguished twenty-nine-year-old Spanish soldier could stand before a rapacious Berber merchant and coax him from his usual careless cruelty to such a show of mercy? Was there a warmth and sincerity in his eyes, in his voice, in his face, that leaped the impossible distance from slave to owner, from Christian to Berber? Or did the greedy Dali Mami simply cherish the hope that he could still gain five hundred ducats in ransom money by keeping Miguel alive?

From this distance, of course, it is almost impossible to say. Perhaps there was a little of both mercy and greed in Dali Mami's clemency.

One thing we do know, however. Twenty-five years later, when Miguel Cervantes was writing the novel that encompassed so much of what he had seen and thought and experienced in his life, he made quite an adventure out of his experiences in Algeria. Don Quixote, his hero, was not himself captured by any pirates, but in the course of his wanderings about as a knight-errant, he met a man who had been a captive.

As this captive tells his tale to the fascinated Don Quixote, we not only get a good many clues as to what Miguel's own imprisonment was like; we get a flashing reference to Miguel himself. Sitting in his Madrid cell, writing his book, the gray, bearded Cervantes has not been able to resist the joke. Smiling, tongue-in-cheek, he makes the captive say: "The only person who made out well with our master was a Spanish soldier by the name of Saavedra, for although this man had done things which will remain in the memory of that people for years to come, and all by way of obtaining his liberty, yet the Moor never dealt him a blow, nor ordered him flogged. . . . And for the least of the many things that Saavedra did, we were all afraid that he would be impaled, and he himself feared it more than once."

Thus did Don Miguel pay half-mocking tribute to the young man he had been. One frustrated attempt to escape Dali Mami had simply led him to try once again. But this second attempt was also a failure. And still . . . "the Moor never dealt him a blow."

His second failure led Miguel to think of still another plan for flight, this time on the grandest scale of all—a scale of such proportions that it would involve dozens of Christian captives from all over Algiers. His plan was to enable all of them to escape on a chartered ship.

In Cervantes' book, Don Quixote's captive tells a tale involving many of the elements which were undoubtedly part of Miguel's own plan. The captive recounts various details: overlooking the courtyard where the captive was held, he says, were the windows of a house belonging to a wealthy Moor of high rank. From these windows the captive and his fellows have been observed by the Moor's beautiful daughter (who is secretly a Christian, thanks to the teaching of a long-dead nurse). This beautiful damsel falls in love with the handsome captive in the courtyard, and by means of notes dropped from her window, makes it clear she will help him and his fellows escape

—if he will take her with them. When the captive replies that he is only too glad to cooperate, she lowers much gold, wrapped in her kerchiefs; she helps him with his plan to charter a ship.

Alas, there was probably no beautiful Moorish maiden involved in Miguel's plot, but even as with the first attempt to escape, he needed an ally in Dali Mami's household. He also needed all the friendliness on the part of the guards which he had managed to achieve. One of the guards in particular had a special fondness for Miguel, since it was he who had brought him the happy news that Rodrigo was alive and well in another Moorish home in Algiers.

With this ally in Dali Mami's household and with the other guards willing to look away now and then, Miguel managed to make contact with a helpful renegade in the city. This made it possible for him to send out letters and messages to various Christian settlements along the Algerian coast, asking for help with the escape plan.

One way and another—slowly, painstakingly—promises of help were collected: promises of money, promises of cooperation. The word went out on that strange grapevine which seems to spring up wherever men are imprisoned, through all the courtyards of Algiers. The plot was progressing. Friends far up the coast had already chartered a ship. Of course it was disguised as a harmless coastal trader, but as soon as all the captives who were joining in the escape had made their way to the appointed rendezvous, the ship would weigh anchor and sail for Spain.

Dedicated, relentless, meticulous about detail, Miguel was now using all the qualities that might have made him a really brilliant commanding officer if his fortunes as a soldier had not gone awry.

"You have courage, intelligence, a level head," Monsignore Aquaviva had said, long ago in Rome. "You should be a good soldier. *You just need luck.*"

Miguel needed that luck now. For at last everything was in readiness and the plot was to be put into action. The signal went out to prisoners all over Algiers. "Tonight is the night."

On that night, late, Miguel gave the signal to the breathless men around him which meant it was time to start scaling the wall of the courtyard enclosure. At the same moment, throughout the city, scores of other prisoners silently climbed the walls of their courtyard prisons. From here, there and everywhere, they made their swift but silent way to the house of a Christian farmer outside Algiers. Here they were to hide during the following day.

Great was the rejoicing among them all, as each man slipped quietly into the farmhouse, and as quietly hid himself behind the trestle-work of its narrow corridors.

But scarcely had the last man joined the group when Miguel heard the far-off echo of trumpets. He held his breath. Perhaps it was nothing. There was no reason to jump to the conclusion that the sound signaled an alarm.

Soon enough, however, such a conclusion could not be denied. Trembling behind the lattices, the hapless Christians heard the trumpet sound nearer and nearer, heard also the hoarse braying of sharply spurred camels. Then they saw the clouds of dust which signalled the swift approach of hordes of Turkish soldiers.

They had been betrayed. No time now to wonder by whom, or how, or when. They were not in a sanctuary, they were in a trap!

Now the soldiers were surrounding the men, seizing them roughly, taking them back to Algiers. And they were going back, not to their individual owners, but to face the judgment of Hassan Pasha, the Viceroy of Algiers.

Hassan Pasha, dreaded by Christians and Berbers alike, was the Turkish governor of the province, who chose to show his mastery over this strange land and people by a course of unremitting cruelty.

When, in Cervantes' story, Don Quixote's captive spoke of the king of Algiers, he might have been speaking of this ruler . . . "Each day he hanged this man, impaled one, cut off the ear of another, and all this with so little excuse, or with none at all, that the Turks had to admit he did it simply to be doing it, inasmuch as their natural bent towards the entire human race is a homicidal one."

Certainly it was a man of this type, a man whose ferocity had become legendary, before whom Miguel was now to be summoned. Miguel, the guards made it clear, was going to have to answer for more than an attempted escape. The scale on which he had planned his effort made it almost a rebellion. Certainly he had organized a

far-reaching conspiracy that had roused an entire district of Algiers. Hassan Pasha had strung up many men on the gallows for merely dreaming of such a thing.

So Miguel stood before Hassan Pasha to answer for his crime. He began to speak, quietly, as he had spoken to Dali Mami. And even as with Dali Mami, he did not try to justify himself. He spoke only on behalf of the others who had fled with him, seeking pardon for them.

What was his magic? What was the secret quality that had enabled him to flout the Moor who still "never dealt him a blow nor ordered him flogged"? What *was* it that came across now to the redoubtable monster of Algiers, so that Hassan Pasha stared at him and listened as a man in a dream?

Was it because Miguel stood there in such jeopardy and did not tremble for himself? Or was it because, for once, Hassan Pasha heard a man speaking to him as one human being to another? In all his years as governor of the province, he had met with only servility and flattery. Now he was listening to a man who spoke freely and simply; who was honest, upright, and full of human warmth—even for him.

Whatever the magic was, the Pasha was as unable to resist as Dali Mami had been. Miguel spoke out as though he believed that the Pasha was a human being who knew and loved mercy and peace. In an inner revolt more momentous than the one which had stirred the captives, something in the Pasha's heart stirred and responded to this man's words.

The end was that the Pasha kept Miguel in his own custody, ordering the rest of the prisoners returned to their owners. Let the world interpret his motive as it would, calling it weakness or whim, the fact remains that the Pasha decided to spare the Spaniard.

He paid Dali Mami the five hundred ducats which was Miguel de Cervantes' ransom price. Thenceforth Miguel was the slave of Hassan Pasha, living in the seraglio.

8

IN WHICH *our hero becomes the "luck" of Hassan Pasha, and struggles to escape from a life of ease.*

HASSAN PASHA, the ruler, or Bey, of Algiers, lived within the fortified walls of the Casbah. His rich palace there had vast enclosed quarters that were known as the seraglio. For Miguel, stepping into the seraglio was like entering a strange, unreal world, a world that truly seemed to lie under one of those enchantments that would one day be so dear to the heart of his knight, Don Quixote.

Everywhere there was such beauty, such luxury, that Miguel felt bewildered. Once again, as so often in his life, beliefs and standards that had been taken for granted were toppling under the impact of what he actually saw and realized with his own senses. All his life long he had been nurtured on the idea that Turks and Moors were barbarians, heathens from whom nothing that was good could possibly be expected. But could they be barbarians who, with infinite patience and love, had adorned every wall, every pillar, every window and niche with such enchanting ornaments, sculpture and designs, as he saw now in the seraglio?

Miguel had seen Moorish architecture before, of course—Spain was full of it. The buildings in Seville, Granada and Cordoba were almost all Moorish. But there, surrounded by prejudice against the despised Moors, he had looked at their creations without really seeing them. Had he then been asked about the Moorish palaces and mosques, he probably would have responded like any Spaniard— called them barbaric, odd, extravagant, yes—but never beautiful.

But now he was living in the heart of such a palace. Endless hours of leisure enclosed him, and his senses were awake with that peculiar sensitivity which often follows release from tension. In the reaction from all the fevered excitement of the escape and the arrest, he wandered about the arcades and terraces of the seraglio, marveling

105

at all he saw. Not only was there a wealth of beauty, created with
infinite care; this beauty was useful too. The delicate arcades provided shelter from the sun, the ornate fountains cooled the air, and
the bright green of the foliage rested the eyes. Graceful creatures,
gazelles and peacocks, wandered about the seraglio, enlivening the
scene without disturbing its calm; gay colors induced a happy mood
in the beholder. Looking at all this, with eyes that truly saw, it was
hard for Miguel not to realize the ironical fact that much of the best
in Spanish art was adapted from Arabic models. He smiled a little to
himself. These were heretical thoughts indeed. Here he was, a prisoner of a Turkish pasha, coming to the conclusion that it was too bad
the Moors had been chased out of Spain!

Of course it was a very odd sort of imprisonment that he suffered.
No more than at Dali Mami's was he required to do any sort of work,
and here he was allowed to mingle freely with guards and other at-

tendants. Occasionally he was summoned to the Pasha's presence to act as an interpreter, or to assist in composing a document, for the Bey had discovered very quickly that Miguel knew several languages and was adept at letter-writing.

These sessions were sometimes prolonged when the Bey fell into conversation with Miguel. It soon became clear that Hassan was fascinated by his new slave, who had pleaded so eloquently for his fellow prisoners. The Bey would ask Miguel about his life in Spain, or in Rome, or about his career as a soldier. And just as Miguel's gift for fresh and colorful phrases had intrigued the Madrid intellectuals years ago, so they delighted this Turkish ruler. One day, Hassan asked Miguel if he played chess. When it turned out that he did, Hassan often summoned him for a game.

So it was that Miguel's privileges in the seraglio were constantly increased. He was free to move throughout the palace and through its extensive gardens. If he wanted books or paper or pen, he had only to ask for them. It was truly an enchanted kind of imprisonment —with just one ugly, jarring fact. When the Bey had bought him for Dali Mami's ransom price, five hundred ducats, he, in turn, had put his own ransom price on Miguel—a ransom price just double the

original. If five hundred had been out of proportion, a thousand ducats was simply preposterous. Miguel wandered through the paradise of his prison, his mind obsessed by the problem of how he could ever obtain his freedom with such a price upon it.

A thousand ducats! Why, one single ducat alone could buy two fine cows at home in Spain. Two or three ducats could see a family through an entire year, as far as the necessities of living. Still, Miguel had seen and heard enough about the wealthy to know that there were also those who thought nothing of spending ten times such a ransom fee on one feast alone. Pacing back and forth along the cool arcades, Miguel's desperate fancy conjured up a grandee, giving way to a whim, freeing him in one casual, generous gesture. But where was he to find the grandee? And how, even if he found one, would he set about encouraging the one generous, necessary gesture?

Sometimes, while playing chess, Miguel would plead with Hassan to lower his ransom. It amused the Bey that this Spaniard had a talent for using almost any incident as a springboard to the subject nearest his heart. Sometimes he would even applaud some especially clever variation in Miguel's request. But he never committed himself. Instead, the Bey would tell Miguel that the matter was all in Allah's hands, Allah be praised; or he would comfort him with a story of a strange case which had seemed hopeless but ended well.

Once, after a game which Miguel had seemed certain to lose but which he succeeded in winning by a near-miracle, Hassan said, "This game you ought to remember. Just as you were trapped, and there was apparently no hope, nevertheless you came out victorious. Today you are still in bondage, but some day, Allah providing, you will be free."

Miguel could only smile wearily. Obviously it was hopeless to plead with this strange despot. But obviously, too, it was impossible to adopt the fatality of the Mohammedan and leave it all to Kismet—fate—or the will of Allah. He had to keep prying and prodding at the problem—until, somehow, it yielded a solution.

One day a new plan came to him, a very curious plan. He began to collect all the information he could about the Algerian coast line. He learned the positions of the garrisons, the hours of the watches, how many guns defended each fortress. In his privileged position, it was not too difficult to gain these facts, but it took time. Then, when he had the information collected, he sat down and composed it all into a long poem, which told exactly how the coast could be conquered.

When the poem was finished, in one careful, well-wrought stanza after another, he copied it all out fairly, and sent it off to—His Majesty, King Philip of Spain!

What was his hope from such an odd endeavor? Why did he send off a perfectly sensible plan in the form of poetry? Perhaps he was hoping that in this guise it would pass any censors, who would not dream of reading poetry. Perhaps he hoped that when it reached the King's palace, the poetic form would serve to draw attention to his message and increase its chances of being read. Then, once the message had been read and its importance grasped, surely Miguel must have nourished the hope that the King's attention would be directed to the composer of the poem. "Who is he?" he could imagine the King asking. "A captive of the Bey? See to it that he is ransomed at once!"

Whatever the fond hopes with which Miguel sent off his poem, not one of them materialized. The poem arrived in Madrid, and attracted absolutely no attention at all. Some secretary glanced at it, gave it a number, and filed it with other unlikely letters to the King. And that was that.

In the seraglio of the Bey, Miguel knew nothing of this, of course, and he kept alive his hopes for the letter as long as he could. And the days went on, the weeks went on, and the unreality of his life enclosed him like a dream. He tried to read, to study the Arabic language and culture. All sorts of books were at his disposal, and he told himself that making an intellectual effort would be good for him. So he sat with his books, trying to concentrate. And then, seemingly from nowhere, he would hear music—music that lifted and fell in a strange, exotic melody. Or the air would suddenly eddy with a drift of sweet, intoxicating fragrance. Where did the music and the scent come from? Who knew? It was part of the enchantment.

Or, another time, as he sat by the shrubs and flowers near the fountain, brightly clad Nubian servants would suddenly approach on silent feet and indicate that he must leave this spot. From a distance then, after he had gone to another part of the seraglio, he would hear the light voices of women as they approached the fountain. They were Hassan's wives, amusing themselves with a brief excursion from the harem. They bathed and sang, called to the birds

and gazelles—and then suddenly they were gone again, as swiftly as they had come.

It was a dream, all of it . . . the armed Nubian guards, the voices, the music, the sweet aromas, the gentle breezes. And he himself, in the midst of all these visions, was he any more real than these many-colored fantasies? Miguel gazed at the quiet goldfish, the gazelles and peacocks—then looked down at himself. Was this really he, this man in silken Moorish attire? Had he ever been a soldier, sailed on a man-of-war, and smelled the acrid smoke of gunpowder? What *was* reality? Was it the outer shape and look of things—a power so strong it could mold the very spirit of man? Or was man's spirit stronger, triumphantly real no matter how the solid world denied it?

Years later, Miguel's knight, Don Quixote, was to fight that battle up and down all Spain, invincibly committed to the spirit. His adventures were wildly comic to all observers, and to all who read about them, too. What could be more absurd than a man battling a herd of sheep, convinced it was an army? What could be more lunatic than this man bowing before a rowdy peasant girl, convinced it was his noble lady love, Dulcinea (herself a figment of his imagination), cruelly disguised by a wicked enchanter? It *was* lunatic, of course—and yet, somehow, the fidelity of the knight's devotion to his ideal shone brighter than all the folly; so that beyond all the laughter there was finally something else—respect, or envy, or even love.

The spirit! It *had* to be the spirit. Standing in the languorous, murmuring stillness of the seraglio, Miguel would suddenly wrench himself away from his doubts. He was Miguel de Cervantes y Saavedra, a soldier of the King, and there *were* things this man and this soldier could do to prove it. He could write letters—to the family at home, to friends in Spain—to Rodrigo, who was not so far away as they, but still suffering, even as he, under the weight of captivity.

Then, once the letters were written, he would have a valid excuse for a visit to the Christian quarter of Algiers. This was a visit that always brought him back to the real world. As soon as the heavy gate of the Casbah closed behind him and he stood in the torrid, sun-drenched world outside, his spirits revived. His guards kept two or three steps behind him at all times, but he paid no attention to them. They did not partake of this reality; they belonged to the other world, behind the gate.

Buoyantly, but without haste, Miguel would stride into the city,

into the noise, the dirt and the stench. Things that ordinarily would have offended him he welcomed now—the smell of rancid oil, garlic, camel dung and dead fish. From a thousand kitchens came whiffs of smoke and mutton fat, and from the shops the odor of wine and onions. He was jostled and pushed. He plunged into a bedlam of braying donkeys, barking dogs, creaking ox carts and shouting peddlers. He heard the din of the blacksmith's hammer, the clang of the coppersmith's tools. He pressed through crowds of yelling children and cackling hens, past camels swarming with flies.

This was the real world, life as it was; not a beautiful world, but he loved it nonetheless. Later, when Cervantes created his knight, Don Quixote, a man devoted to the spirit, he gave him a squire who came from this real world, a round and practical little man named Sancho Panza. Not the brightest fellow you could find—hardly given to abstract thought, and much addicted to proverbs, Sancho Panza still was as solid as earth, giving support to all Don Quixote's flighty schemes. Yes, it took both to make reality—a soaring, questing spirit —but iron pots, too, kitchen fires, and bread in the belly.

And then, on one of Miguel's visits to a Christian merchant with whom he had become friendly, he heard wonderful news! Ransom money had arrived from Spain—three hundred ducats. *Three hundred!* His family must have made incredible sacrifices to collect that

sum—and yet it would not even begin to meet the ransom price Hassan Pasha demanded for him. Three hundred . . . it was no good at all to Miguel, but it *would* be enough to pay the ransom for Rodrigo. Someone must quickly carry the news to the house where Rodrigo was imprisoned! His brother would be free at last.

Miguel was almost as happy to have Rodrigo free as if he were free himself. All through the months and years of their captivity, he had been worrying about Rodrigo, so sturdy of limb, so used to a life of action. With his strong and healthy body he was fit for any kind of hard labor, and it was amazing that he had not been chained to the oars of a galley long since. If that had happened, there was more than just the agonizing labor to fear. Miguel had trembled, thinking of Rodrigo's impulsiveness. Pressed too far, there was no telling how he might rebel. But now he was free!

Miguel turned his own steps back towards the Casbah, glad for his brother, but feeling his own captivity like the weight of a stone. He looked up into the yellow evening sky—and, in a sudden, desperate moment, he believed he was ready to end the non-reality of his existence in the reality of death. It would be so easy—a sword or a dagger quietly borrowed from one of the guards, then swiftly, before anyone could guess, the dagger plunging—but no. He was a Christian and such an act was a sin. He did not have the right to be his own executioner. He was a burden to himself, but he had to bear that burden. The why or the wherefore did not signify. He only knew he *had* to hold out.

In the months that followed, Miguel began to go more frequently into the city, both to forward letters and to visit a father confessor. More and more Christians in the city began to recognize him and to know him. They knew his singular fate—how he had forfeited his life, and yet had become a confidante of the Bey. They knew he was a devout Christian, and many marveled at his constancy, for in his position it would have been easy for him to obtain his freedom simply by adopting the Moslem faith. Hundreds had done this and had fared very well. But somehow no one thought of suggesting this to Miguel. For himself, the idea never entered his mind. Knowing all they did about him, these Christians wondered who he really was. An individual of high rank? He denied it, said he was only a worthless soldier of the King. But worthless was the one thing nobody would believe that he was.

In time, so many of the men in the Christian quarter had become friendly with Miguel—not just merchants and traders, but monks and priests as well—that they began to seriously consider whether they could not help this unusual man win his freedom. It was true that he was a favorite of the Pasha, but the Pasha was hardly a man to rely on. At any moment, for some reason or other, he might feel constrained to change his leniency to harshness. Besides, his term as Viceroy was almost over. When he left Algiers, who knew what might happen to Don Miguel? Yes, it was high time his friends banded together and interested themselves in his case!

So it was that, early one autumn morning, Miguel was summoned to the gate of the Casbah. There a Berber youth stood waiting for him. The lad told him that he must go into the city because more ransom money had been offered.

Miguel dared not believe it. He would not let himself give way to the excitement and hope that welled up in him. But as soon as he could, he hastened to the city. It was true! More ransom money had come from his family. It was a small enough sum, but how it had been achieved, in addition to the three hundred ducats already sent, heaven only knew. But this was not all the money available. For the first time, he learned that the Christians in Algiers were collecting money for him and were ready to negotiate with the Bey in his behalf.

The bargaining process was long and exhausting. The Bey could have waived the money; he was enormously wealthy. But the prospect of losing his favorite slave drove him to frenzies of stubbornness. He was seized with the notion that Miguel brought him luck—how *could* he part with such a talisman? "I need him!" he cried, over

115

and over. "I need him. As long as the Spaniard is around, I have nothing to fear."

But the Christians kept on pressing their case with pleas and protestations. Finally, they managed to wheedle Hassan's price down to six hundred ducats. Hassan clapped his hands upon his silken knees. That was his last word—that was final. Six hundred ducats, if they wanted his Spaniard.

Even this sum was considerably larger than the amount Miguel's family and the Christian merchants had collected together. And

then, when everything looked hopeless, the Franciscan monks came to the rescue. They had some money which had been assigned for another prisoner's ransom, but since it was not enough to free him, they donated it for Miguel's release.

He was free!

That night, tasting freedom again, he looked up at the stars; they seemed to belong to him. All earth and all heaven seemed to belong to him. He breathed the air in a new way, greeted the morning like a new man. He overflowed with love for everything he saw around him. He had to restrain himself from leaping for joy, slapping his thighs and turning somersaults.

But now came the trying period of waiting for many papers: a letter of remission, certificates of good conduct, safe-conduct passes, other legal documents and receipts. Without them, he ran the risk of again falling into the hands of the first Barbary pirates who came along. He also needed papers from the Spanish authorities: letters of recommendation from the monks and the Christian merchants, and affidavits of his religious integrity. Then it was time to thank—so many people, known and unknown—who had labored on his behalf.

At last the wonderful, unbelievable moment came. He stood at a ship's railing, waving good-by, while the ship's sails were unfurled to catch the breeze. He could still discern the figures of several of his friends who had come to see him off. Then the morning mist came between the ship and the shore—and soon Algiers sank below the horizon.

9

IN WHICH *it is told how Don Miguel returned home, and what happened there.*

D ON MIGUEL DE CERVANTES was thirty-three years old when his captivity finally ended and he sailed at last for home. He had been away from Spain twelve years altogether: five years as a captive, five years in the army, two years with Monsignore Aquaviva in Rome. Twelve years! It was a long time. As he came nearer to his homeland he began to realize that all the while he had been gone he had remembered his family, his friends and his country as they were when he left them. Unaltering, they had lived on in his memory exactly as he had last seen them. But now he must prepare himself for the changes time must have made in them—as it had made in him.

Also, he must think of what he was going to do now. For so long, all plans for the future had been so impossible it seemed unbelievable that it was time for them at last. Through the years in Algiers he had called himself a soldier. Was he to go back to soldiering? It was what he wanted—the bravest calling of all. But he faced fact: a lieutenant thirty-three-years old was ridiculous. Many of his former comrades must now be colonels who had fought in many places. They would have real experience. He had none.

There was something else that made Miguel hesitate. The events of the last years had indeed changed him, made him too able, perhaps, to understand both sides of an issue. The thought that if he did return to the army, he might well be stationed in Flanders, forced to shoot the Netherlanders simply because they had chosen a different religion from his, made him wince. He was proud of being a soldier, but he no longer knew what could be called a just cause for war. Too many solemn reasons given were mere pretexts, too many wars were fought only in the interests of the princes.

His own indecision confused him. He could not afford to be indecisive. He had obligations to meet, or so he felt. His family had made enormous sacrifices to save him. Others must have helped to raise the funds for his freedom. He had to find ways to pay back what he owed, although the debt looked hopelessly large.

For just a moment, Miguel allowed himself to think about what he might do if he had no obligations. He remembered the happiness he had always known with paper and a pen, writing poetry. How pleasant it would be to sit at a desk, at home in Madrid, juggling words and fancies as the performers at the kermesses juggled their bright balls. Deep in his heart, he felt he had a talent for writing; certainly the impulse was often with him to set forth in memorable phrases what he saw and imagined.

Or perhaps, instead of poetry, it would be exciting to try his hand at writing a play. His playwright friends in the Madrid cafés had once talked as though he might have a flair for the stage—certainly he loved the theater. A play—but this was folly! This was madness. A man could not count on earning money from writing. And Miguel had his obligations. His duties, too—to country and King. He had sworn the oath to obey. If he could not serve as an active soldier, he must find a way to serve somehow.

So he made his decision. And then, leaning on the rail, he saw a somber line across the horizon. Land. Spain. Home.

He had looked forward to this day for so long, savoring the thoughts of homecoming. Now, with the moment actually arriving, everything seemed to go so fast. The coast line flew towards him—nearer, clearer every second.

Then, suddenly, he was sitting with many others in a small boat, being rowed to shore—Miguel de Cervantes, an ill-clad Spaniard from North Africa, who did not own a single piece of baggage. The prow of the boat grated on the sand, and Miguel had to leap out, to rush quickly up the beach, for others behind him were pushing impatiently, eager to be on shore.

So Miguel stood on Spanish soil once more, his eyes moist, filled with an urge to get down on his knees and to utter a prayer of thanksgiving. He wanted to touch the very dust under his feet—but all around him swarmed porters, oarsmen and passengers, and crowds waiting to greet them. Should he behave like a mountebank in front of so many people? No, he must control himself. He pressed through

the throng, hurrying into the city. But as he strode along, he repressed a great sob, for he was aware of being a stranger in his native land.

Fortunately, Miguel had no time to indulge his emotion. He had to busy himself with obtaining provisions and arranging the land journey to Madrid. It was good to hear Spanish spoken, and to pay out money in *réales* and *maravedis*. It warmed his heart to see the fresh fruits and the household articles he had known from boyhood. Only now did he realize fully the strangeness of the land from which he had returned.

A few days later, Miguel was in Madrid. And stood before the house—*his* house. Although his family knew that he was due to arrive soon, the day and hour of his coming were uncertain. He hesitated at the door, suddenly fearful of entering.

Then the door was flung open from the inside, and someone was crying, "Miguel!" There were arms around his neck, and he felt his mother's trembling hands, sensed her sobs, then saw her aging face. His sisters were crowding behind her, crying out his name. And from behind them, from the interior of the house, came his father's deeper voice. "Is he here? Is he here?"

Miguel must now be tended and coddled, and served the choicest foods. He was the most important person in the world, the homecoming hero, the returning Ulysses, for whom nothing was too good.

For a little while, for several days, in fact, Miguel let himself be pampered, for his family's sake if not his own. It would have been cruel of him to deprive his mother and sisters of the pleasure they found in waiting on him. But he could not bear it for long.

All too soon it was plain what poverty his family now knew. He saw the patches on his mother's and sisters' clothing, recognized the cloth from Rodrigo's old doublets that had been altered into women's bodices. He saw worn-out shoes, work-worn hands. And everywhere in the house he noticed that old things were missing: familiar pieces of furniture no longer in their accustomed places, no longer anywhere to be seen. When he asked questions, his mother and father would shake their heads, smiling ruefully. There was no need, really, to say anything. This was the price they had had to pay to collect money for his ransom, and for Rodrigo's, and they refused to regret it. But their sacrifices tore at Miguel's heart—to see them pushed to the ragged edge—all for him and for their eldest son. Rodrigo was back in the army now, sending home what money he could. It was time for Miguel to help too.

"There is no hurry," said his father. "No hurry," echoed his mother, pushing him back in his chair. But it was impossible to stay still, the privileged man of leisure, when such a debt remained, and when everyone else was so constantly busy.

His father, who had aged considerably, was up and about early in the morning, every day, as lean and irritable as he had always been. He grumbled at everything—the authorities, the Church, and, of course, at his patients. But he was off on his visits to the sick as soon as he had finished breakfast, and nothing on earth could have delayed him.

His mother, now in her late fifties, hurried about the house from dawn till dark, as she had always done, but lines of bitterness and unhappiness dragged at her face. It was so clear, so very clear, that

121

nothing in her life had gone as she expected it to. For all her efforts to maintain the standing and standards of nobility, what did she have behind the outward show of respectability she had fought so long to maintain? Nothing but the same old, unending drudgery.

Neither of the girls had married, as their mother had hoped they might. Being daughters of a noble family, they were obliged to be choosey in the matter of suitors. Hardly any husband was considered good enough for them. But since they had no dowry to offer, no prospective husbands, suitable or otherwise, confused the situation by presenting themselves.

As a result, poor Andrea and Luisa were spinsters now, still under the thumb of their mother—who ordered them about the house, but never let them out of it, except for Mass. The twelve years Miguel had been away was a longer time for them than for him, really. Andrea was matronly now, her proud self-righteousness even more evident. Since the possibility of marriage had always seemed remote to her, she herself had chosen to rule it out of her life, and had entered, of her own accord, into a marriage with Heaven. She had not formally joined any religious order, but she wore a nun's habit and went daily to Mass. Luisa, her prettiness faded a little, still managed to have a more cheerful time in life than the others, probably because she was willing to giggle at trifles.

These were the ones who, having little enough to start with, had deprived themselves still further to save Miguel. There was a harshness to this fact, an injustice to it, that made Miguel think his liberty had been bought much too dearly. He should not have taken it at such a price. But then, he told himself, he had had to accept it as the will of Providence; he must not be ungrateful.

Brushing aside his family's protests, he at once started his campaign to get back into service. Every day he went out, making appointments to see old friends, old acquaintances, or new persons who might be able to help him.

He visited his old friend, General Figueroa, who was in Madrid, and anxiously broached the subject of the army promotion which had seemed so near—five long years ago. The General frowned, looked out the window, spoke unhappily. Unfortunately, five years changed many things. Much as he would like to gratify Don Miguel, the situation was really not favorable now. But he would see what he could do about recommending him for *some* kind of post in the King's service. And here were the names of other men of influence who might be of help. He was indeed glad to see Don Miguel back safely after his terrible experiences. He wished him the best of luck.

Smiling a little stiffly, hoping not to betray his disappointment, Miguel bowed his way out. And went on, quickly, before he had time to be stopped by discouragement, to see about appointments with all the men mentioned by General Figueroa.

It was a toilsome time, a miserable time, utilizing every possible influence, every recommendation, however slight, in the hope of obtaining a position. There began to be a kind of agony in hearing, again and again, the same formal assurances of good will—with never anything more substantial.

Only one aspect of these dreary days brightened Miguel's heavy spirit. He was meeting again his old friends and acquaintances of the cafés. Miguel was surprised and moved to see how well all these

men remembered him, and he warmed to the genuine pleasure they showed in welcoming him back.

They may not have missed him as sorely as they claimed, but now that he had returned he was one of them again, as he had been when a youth. And now, when he sat down at a table with them, there was eager clamor to hear all about his many experiences since he had left them. Men from nearby tables quickly clustered around to hear the stories.

Always Miguel had had the trick of amusing them with his fresh phrases and new insights. Now, it seemed that his gift for story-telling had ripened and improved. No matter how many times he told about his capture by the Berbers, or his chess games with the Bey, or that last, fantastic attempt to escape—sometimes he was asked to tell the same story, over and over, on the same day—he always managed to supply new overtones, fresh jokes, different details. Not only that. The trick he had learned in Algiers, of acting out some part of a story for which he had no words, was part of him now. He *acted* the moody Bey, the harem guard, or the street merchants of Algeria.

Thus, to his listeners he conjured up a strange and far-off land, making it tangible and close, and the writers of the group went from simple suggestion to outright pleading: Miguel ought to write down some of these stories. The playwrights pressed him especially hard. There was drama—wonderful, fantastic drama—in all this material he had collected.

Material? Miguel was a little taken aback by the word, and by the concept of these men. He had never once thought of his experiences as *material*—to be worked over, twisted, cut and shaped to the demands of a plot. They were his own life—days and hours during which he had suffered, prayed, and dreamed of home. It was one thing to relate them humorously to his friends; another thing entirely to stand off from them, to see them objectively as ingredients of melodrama or farce. They were too close to him still, too clear in their actual reality, to be reshaped as fiction.

"But it is there, it is all there," his friends kept insisting. "A play —laid in Algiers—how could it fail?"

Miguel remained silent. There was temptation in the thought of trying to write a play. Perhaps, somehow, he could learn to think about his experiences in terms of drama. And then—but no. He got up from the table. He had other tasks, other obligations, that writing

could not fulfill. He would try once more to see the man who had refused to see him yesterday. . . .

So, the dreary round would start again, one hopeless interview after another, one arrogant scribe after another to be faced, some of them so stupid they could not even spell the unheard-of word, *Lepanto*.

Then, when it seemed he could not bear it any longer, his old friend General Figueroa summoned him. The General, at least, had followed through on his expressions of good will. At last he had good

news for Don Miguel. He had the happiness of informing him that he had been chosen for a diplomatic mission which would take him to Oran, on the African coast.

Miguel felt the happy news, in the form of a shock, spread through him like an intoxicant. What did it matter that, as General Figueroa was explaining, the assignment was not of extreme importance in itself? It gave back to Miguel a justified feeling of dignity. More important than any honor entailed, more important even than the money, was the realization that he was trusted; qualified to give his service to the King.

He had been haunted by the fear that he had become useless, whether because of his crippled hand or because of his meager experience as a soldier. Now he had a chance to make himself known, to prove his cunning and valor.

126

10

IN WHICH *our hero tries to discover why a rich country is poor, and solve other diverse problems.*

THERE WAS a certain poetic justice for Don Miguel in going back to North Africa as a free man. To every scene and every meeting it gave a new dimension to be viewing it as an emissary of the King of Spain instead of as a slave. Now, many sights had a beauty and a pageantry of which he had not been conscious at all when he was owned by Dali Mami or the Bey. However, one sight he could not behold without shuddering was a slave market, or a group of slaves on their way to a fate such as his had been—or worse.

His work in Oran was not too difficult, nor did it take long to complete. Returning to Madrid, he was delighted to be charged with a new mission almost at once. This assignment took him to nearby Portugal for several months. It was still so good to be busy, and to be working with a purpose, that Miguel returned to Madrid, eagerly anticipating his next assignment. He had visions of going on and on like this, through the years, his missions increasing in difficulty, his pleasure in them increasing proportionately.

This time, however, there was no new assignment waiting for him. For the first few weeks after his return, Miguel was not troubled by the delay. Then the weeks became a month, two months—and he began to be a little alarmed.

"I am sorry. There does not seem to be anything more for you right now," the official with whom he had been dealing said politely; and promised, of course, to keep him in mind. But how was it possible that there was nothing, nothing anywhere, that he could do for his country? Spain's empire sprawled across half the world, its furthermost boundaries the peaks of the South American Andes. Spain's regiments were everywhere—in France, in Italy, the Netherlands, Hungary. There were Spanish regiments, Spanish governors, teeming centers of Spanish activity in Mexico and Peru. Surely, somewhere, there was *something* Don Miguel de Cervantes could do.

Undoubtedly it was simply a matter of appearing in the right place, of refreshing the memories of those who already knew him, at the right time. Which meant he must show more initiative in pressing his suit. He must do as all his acquaintances advised him: draw up petitions to present to all sorts of men of influence, whether he knew them or not; petitions which would elaborate in detail all the ways in which Miguel had served his country—and which would veritably stun the reader with his merits and accomplishments.

It was a nerve-racking task for Miguel, sitting down to compose documents of such overblown self-importance. Every skill he had with words deserted him, and he labored over the petitions with almost physical pain. Here he was, a man who felt himself a debtor, not only to his family but to his country. All he wanted was a chance to pay off his obligations to that country with faithful service. Instead, he was forced into the position of an irksome petitioner, jostling, pushing and shouting his own merits in order to have his share of the spoils.

And composing the pleas and petitions was only the start of it. Between him and the men who actually allotted posts was a whole network of offices and a battery of secretaries, each man intent on parading his own petty authority. Before the Bey of Algiers, before his own King, Miguel knew he could stand erect. Before these secretaries he had to bow low in order to have them even notice that he was before them.

It was a strange, tightly knit society which in those days thrived in and around the court in Madrid. Its hierarchy followed a ritual which bore no relation to reality, but which was absolutely compulsory for anyone who wanted to be part of it. It was a world of ramrod dignity, of ceremonious bowing and scraping, of affected smiles and elegant compliments. Gossip and intrigue were far better recommendations for advancement than integrity, straightforwardness or self-respect. Also valuable was the possession of something with which one could bargain for offices or sinecures—the favors, for instance, of a sister or daughter. Whoever was lucky enough to have attractive nieces could rub his hands in satisfaction.

Only gradually did Miguel come to see how completely all this was true—but he had plenty of time for his observations. All day long

he could sit, patiently waiting for the chance to see one secretary, for time had little meaning to those already safely connected with the court. In the anterooms of the court, people met one another, paraded about hoping to be seen by persons of importance; did everything, in fact, but work at anything that might be called constructive. These anterooms were a combination of hotel lobby and stock exchange room, a gathering place, actually, for all the idlers whose patents of nobility gave them entry into the fraternity.

Sitting in the anterooms himself, hour after hour, Miguel would puzzle at the scene before him. How was anything of value ever accomplished in such a setting, he wondered. How *was* the country governed, with men such as these responsible for carrying out its policies?

The King, he heard everywhere, was something else again. The King, Philip II, *El Prudente*, was a worker, indefatigable and tireless. But the King was shut away from all this outer turmoil. He lived at the very heart of the court, in ceremonious solitude, the embodiment of sovereign power. His eyes were red, people said,

from working so late into the night, his back was hunched from bending over his constant writing, his fingers gnarled with gout, his once reddish hair gray and thinning—but he drove himself without a let-up.

This King, unlike the rulers of neighboring lands, seemed consumed by a jealous urge to watch over, and assume responsibility for, everything in his far-flung domain. He was a despot, yes; a despot with absolute power he felt was his by divine right, but he was not a tyrant. He was a new kind of king, actually, with a disciplined attitude to his responsibilities that made him the servant of the kingdom he administered, as well as its head.

Not that anyone expressed it that way then. Instead, Miguel heard the courtiers laughing among themselves at the latest run-in between the King's two chief ministers. How droll of the King to choose as his chief advisers two men who hated each other thoroughly! The King would consult with first one, then the other, confiding the first minister's answer to a problem to the second. Of course this was a very shrewd way to swiftly learn the good and bad of any project— it was the start, actually, of a two-party cabinet, the rudiments of parliament, but the men at court were much more inclined to view everything from a personal angle. The King went ahead and made his own decisions anyway. Why bother to pit the two ministers against each other?

In those days, too, Miguel heard much talk of the Escorial, the great new palace Philip was building twenty miles outside Madrid.

One of Philip's few relaxations was a ride, now and then, to this vast building which was designed to combine a palace, a monastery and a cathedral.

Today, the Escorial is ranked in importance, in dignity and splendor, with the greatest architectural achievements of the West. Yet it is no symbol of luxury or personal power. Instead, in many ways, it reflects the character of the man who built it. Its main portion was a monastery and a cathedral. Even so was Philip's main concern, both at home and abroad, the business of religion. In ruling his kingdom, in the exploits of his army all over the world, the defense of the faith was his prime objective. Defending the faith, extending the faith—all his gigantic labors were motivated by that force, just as the gigantic Escorial was chiefly created for religious use. Only in one wing was a section set apart and furnished for the royal family. The room the King chose for himself was a small, simple workroom, containing nothing but a bed, a table and a chair.

So this stern, austere King labored in his fearful isolation—and in the anterooms the courtiers paraded about, filling the hours with their ceremonious, senseless chatter. And on the outskirts of the anteroom, Miguel waited, watching and wondering what was wrong with a country, so powerful and so rich, that still had no place for him, no matter how patiently he waited.

At home, the family talk always contained a worried note. Prices were so high it seemed they could not go any higher—and then they went up again. Miguel would come home, after an exhausting day of fruitless waiting, to hear his father, Don Rodrigo, complaining that every day his patients grew poorer, more destitute, less able to pay the small fees he charged. Miguel could see it for himself. Everywhere there was poverty—more poverty than he could remember ever seeing before—he who had known its face from childhood.

What was wrong? Spain was rich. Since Cortez and Pizarro had conquered the rich provinces of Mexico and Peru in the New World, a steady river of gold had flowed home to Spain. Where had it gone? Why were so many of the looms that produced Spain's proudest commodity, her precious wool, standing idle? Why were fields lying fallow, mills, wine- and oil-presses standing unused? Why—the question always came back to this—was Miguel standing idle, too, in such a rich country?

Yes, it always came back to this, but, child of his times that he was,

132

there was no way for Miguel to answer his question—no way for him to see behind the great show of power and might to the inner tensions that were driving Spain to bankruptcy in spite of her wealth.

In Rome, it was true, he had heard much grave talk about Spain's extravagant warfare all over the world, wherever Philip might feel the faith was threatened. If the Calvinists grew strong in Poland, Philip felt personally responsible for crushing them. If the Protestants gained the upper hand in France, or anywhere, Philip must rush an army to the scene. This Miguel knew about, and he knew, too, that while the King deemed it important for gold to be shipped from Mexico to Spain, he deemed it far more important that the Indians in Mexico be converted. Obviously, it would be a strain on any exchequer to try to wage war simultaneously in Flanders and Lombardy, in Burgundy and Africa, in America and on the high seas.

But still, though the swordsmiths and harness-makers alone, of all Spain's workers, kept continually busy, they were not getting rich either. The Crown owed all of them money for their efforts in the army's behalf. It owed salaries to its officials and back pay to its soldiers. Where was the gold going?

The gold, it is easy to see now, when all the dust and passion are settled, was going to just a few people at the very top of the heap. Instead of being fairly distributed, it remained in the hands of the grandees, a few wealthy merchants, middlemen and speculators.

As for the Crown, it was deeply in debt. Philip had ascended the throne in a Spain already groaning under its huge debt burden. The coronation of his father as Emperor Charles V had cost an incalculable sum, an outlay for a single individual conceivable only in those days of incredible luxury. Philip himself added to the debt with the extravagance of his warfare. As a result, he was constantly borrowing—here, there and everywhere.

Unused as Miguel was to court ways, and the figures to be expected there, he did not realize how many men he saw who would never have been there a few years before—German, Flemish, Italian and Portugese—men of common birth, not nobility at all, were welcome now because of their wealth. To them, even the doors of the innermost sanctum were unhesitatingly opened. Phillip needed money, and so burghers and merchants from many lands had ready access to his ear—the Welsers and Fuggers from Germany, the Medici from Florence, and many others—**all** of them willing to lend money to the Spanish Empire in return for extraordinary privileges and monopolies.

These men, and their money, were the real reason why Miguel, and many another man like him, had no opportunity to serve the State. The State, deeply indebted to the grandees and the merchants, recruited its officials from these circles—officials who were willing to work for the honor rather than any pay. There was simply not

enough money in the treasury to provide everyone with a good post at an appropriate salary. There was no money to provide every post with the best man for the position. The richest man had to do.

But no one was really aware that this was the actual state of affairs. The gold came in, the prices went up. The rich got richer, the poor got poorer, the King worked later and later every night, and Don Miguel de Cervantes waited, with despair growing like a chancre in his heart, for something to do. He lived in the richest, most powerful country in the world, and it had no place for him, no place at all.

11

IN WHICH *Don Miguel gives up trying for the government post and turns to something much more entertaining!*

ODDLY ENOUGH, it was his continued bad luck that at last turned Miguel to the thing he had dreamed of doing—that is, if he'd had no obligations. At this point it could hardly matter if writing paid little. He was earning nothing as it was. He could not do worse. He might—he just might—have a little luck with the pen.

There was not much to hope for, really. In those days, writers were not supposed to work for gain. Their talent was considered a gift, not to be abused for profit. It was not a craft, like painting, which had a good market and commanded decent prices. The very best a writer could hope for was a purse of gold when he dedicated his work to some prince or grandee. Miguel knew no such powerful figure, but still—writing gave him pleasure, writing required no capital at all, his friends at the cafés had been urging him toward it for a long time—what else should he be doing with his time? So, Don Miguel de Cervantes began seriously to write.

At that time, about 1580, very few plays existed in Spain, and most of these few consisted of primitive farces. Or else they were stilted plays in which every person pretended to be someone else —until the action got so confused that, at the end, a god or a magician was needed to tell the characters who they really were. Of course there were the traditional mystery plays for the important church festivals, all of them very long-winded and boring. In other words, the theater as we know it since the days of Shakespeare (who began his active life about twelve years later) hardly existed in Spain.

Miguel's heart had been with the stage since he was a little boy. It was the stage for which he wanted to write now. But, like a few other men who were beginning to appear here and there, he wanted to create from real life—and he wanted a plot which could be understood. This alone is enough to establish him as one of the first modern authors of Spain. However, for all his desire to experiment with plot, he still chose to write in the traditional language of the stage, which was poetry.

Setting himself to work, Miguel decided that his friends had been right in urging him to make use of some of the colorful scenes with which he had grown familiar during his captivity in Algeria. Soon his first play began to take shape; "The Traffic of Algiers," he called it. Now the days that had crawled with such agonizing slowness in the anterooms of the court sped along, filled with purpose. He sat at a table in his room at home, hardly noticing how his mother and sisters went about, loudly and pointedly asking each other what Miguel could be up to. Doña Leonora's disappointment in her son hardly could be concealed any longer. She had had such great hopes for him when he entered the service of Monsignore Aquaviva—so long ago. She had still nurtured her hopes for him when he joined the army. A nobleman could rise to fame and fortune in the army. Instead of that, there had been his capture by the pirates, the impossible ransom, a few pitiful jobs after his return home, then nothing—nothing, except a poorly clad thirty-five-year-old son who sat in his room, scribbling.

But at last this play of his was finished. And now Don Miguel's spirits, which could alternate between a heavy, thoughtful melancholy, and the sunniest, funniest of good humor, were suddenly swept up into excited enthusiasm. The play was accepted by the manager of a small theatrical group, who gave him for his efforts the lordly sum of a ducat. But what did it matter if the return were small? The manager was also giving him a chance to perform in the play! All Miguel's inborn talent for acting rose to this lure. In no time it turned out that he was directing the play as well. He had discovered a talent he himself had not known he possessed.

This new talent delighted Miguel. There was a wonderful and heady satisfaction in making a play take shape, breathing the life of action, movement and emotion into the baldly recited words. After his own play had been presented (without stirring its audience to any particular frenzies of either joy or disapproval) Miguel turned eagerly to the work of another author, anxious to try his hand at directing someone else's efforts.

After the close of the play, the group decided it was time to go on the road, in the customary fashion of actors of that period. They asked Miguel to go along as their director, and he accepted with joy. The assignment meant a lot of work and little money, and his family was scarcely pleased by this particular turn of events. Still, for Miguel, it was work he loved, and all the time he worked at it he was learning more about the theater. He would continue writing his own plays as he traveled with the troupe, incorporating into them all that he learned.

So once again, as in his childhood, Miguel took to the road, jogging along in a cart, over the highways of Spain. He visited large cities and small—any place where it appeared that the citizens of the

community would respond well to the promise of an evening or two of entertainment.

As director of the company, Miguel's responsibilities were manifold. It was he who chose the plays that would be presented, he who rewrote them, polished them and changed them till he felt they were as effective as they could possibly be. It was he who handled the casting, shifting roles about, soothing the sensibilities which became ruffled in the process. It was he who saw to the costumes, the properties, the arrangements for the stage where the plays would be presented in each town.

In those days, there were no theaters in the small towns dotted across Spain. The plays were presented in any kind of gathering place that was available—sometimes the main room of an inn, sometimes a barn, sometimes a banquet hall. The stage itself was erected by Miguel and his fellow troupers—a narrow platform put together by placing a few boards, side by side, on boxes or kegs, so that the platform was slightly elevated. There were no wings, no backdrops, no scenery. The audience was told where a scene was taking place —in the woods, in a castle, in a dungeon—and imaginations had to do the rest. The props were of the simplest: a chair, a table, a torch, if the play needed such items. Obviously, there were no footlights either. A few wax tapers at the ends of the stage, or a few lanterns hung about nearby gave a fitful light, illuminating the actors who were waiting about offstage, behind the platform, as well as those who were on stage. Such a bald, bleak view of all the proceedings would hardly enchant playgoers of today, but in those times the audience had no trouble in ignoring what was not part of the action, going along quite happily with the illusion on the stage.

Always, when the play began, a deep silence would fall over the audience. People listened with passionate intentness. Everyone felt

a part of what was being acted out on the stage; everyone was concerned and moved. Inevitably, they took sides with various characters during the course of a play, and the original silence would be broken by cries of warning to endangered characters, or shouts of outrage or shame.

To Miguel, it was wonderfully rewarding to appear before such audiences, to shape the plays to their needs and desires. Watching the responses of these men and women and children, he learned how to build and tighten a comic scene, till he had drawn from it all its humorous possibilities, and laughter rolled helplessly through the crowd. He learned how to create scenes of poignancy, testing, by the truest measurement of all, how much more could be communicated in silence or by a mere word than by the longest, most flowery of speeches. Because he was so concerned with making each scene as dramatically effective as it could be, so that each word, each action, each gesture was an integral part of the whole, leading up to the climax, Miguel frowned at one practice common among the actors and actresses.

They too were concerned with getting a response from the audience, but they sought to obtain it by changing various lines of the play as they went along. Whatever they might have learned in the way of local gossip or intrigue after arriving in a given town, they wanted to incorporate into the play—sure, naturally, of surprised and delighted laughter as a result. They liked weaving in comments on current events, politics, or even the weather. In doing this, they were only following the current practice of their time. All actors did it—changing the text so much that it was often difficult to remember what had been its original plan or plot.

But Miguel could not bear this. The comedy, the tragedy, the mood which he had built so carefully, were destroyed or dissipated in a moment by these fanciful excursions. Pleasantly, but very, very firmly, he told his actors and actresses that they were to speak the lines he had written for them—these and no others. In doing this, he was one of the first playwrights of modern times to insist that a play be presented as written.

The members of his troupe were not particularly pleased by the mandate. It inhibited their creative flights and wounded their vanities. But they could not hold out against Miguel, nor could they really be angry at him. Here, in this roving, unstable, emotional kind of life, Miguel's old authority in dealing with people came to

the fore. Just as in the garrison back in Naples, he became the sturdy, central figure on whom everyone depended. Because he himself refused to get angry, it was difficult for quarrels to come to much around him. All of which was very fortunate for this particular little troupe. Living as they did in such close proximity to each other all the time, traveling from town to town in each other's company—performing together, eating together, washing and sleeping and getting up together—it was easy for nerves to rub raw. But Miguel was a stabilizing influence. He helped keep each person aware that, basically, all had one goal in common, the goal of entertainment, and that their devotion to this goal was greater than any petty dissatisfactions with one another.

So the members of the little troupe went on, from town to town, rattling along in their carts over the dusty roads. All day they would jolt and bump along, the sun burning them, or, often, the rain drenching them. In the afternoons, they would draw into a little town, to an inn, there to receive the warm welcome of an always-friendly innkeeper. Of course, after the welcome, the innkeeper frequently hurried to double-lock and bolt his storeroom—actors, for all their charm, had a good deal in common with gypsies and thieves—they were always hungry. And he was generally careful to order his daughters inside, too, and to keep an eye on his wife. Actors were notorious for their lack of morals. But, with these precautions taken,

The
THEATER on the
ROAD

he was ready to hurry forth some food, and to do all he could to help make ready for the evening performance.

There was no monotony in all this for Miguel. Each day and each town, for all they were so like each other, taught him something new—about the theater, about writing, and about people—the people for whom he wrote and the people about whom he wrote. But this was not all that pleased him. There was something else, something that filled him with a strange and heady delight he had never experienced before.

For it was in these days, traversing the roads of Spain with his company of actors, that Miguel finally—and for the first time—fell in love! True, he had admired pretty women before; and he had tried his stumbling best to pay them the gallant compliments they required. He had wondered about love—whether the extravagant poems written in its praise had any relationship at all to what a man and woman might really feel about one another—but, basically, he was very shy of women. He was ready to grant them every respect, but no woman he had ever known—his mother, his sisters, or anyone else—had given him an inkling of tenderness, or beauty linked with warmth, which love could bring.

And now, here he was—head over heels!

Francesca de la Rosa was her name, and of course she was beautiful—dark and beautiful and full of spirit and pride. She had joined the troupe not long after it left Madrid, and it was plain at once that she was different from the other women of the company. There was a grace in her bearing, and a confidence in her manner, that at once stamped her as the daughter of a fine and noble family. But this was incredible! If it was unlikely for a man of noble birth, Don Miguel, for example, to go trouping with actors, it was simply unheard-of for the *daughter* of such a family to go on the stage! It was as though she had leaped off a cliff, or thrown herself in front of runaway horses! She had committed suicide, she was dead, so far as her family was concerned.

But this troubled Francesca not a whit. Perhaps she *was* mad, in that day and that time, to think a woman had a right to freedom, to feel that life was something that must be lived according to the urges of each individual—not according to traditional routine. She was willing to accept all the responsibilities of her fantastic belief, however, and bore the hazards and difficulties of the free life she had

chosen with invincible calm, even gaiety.

Of course Miguel fell in love. And of course, before too long, Francesca admitted, as freely and proudly as she did everything, that she loved him too.

How wonderful it was to jolt along through the now dry and dusty countryside, Francesca at his side, listening, fascinated, to his tales of Algeria, of Rome and Lepanto. How wonderful to work on a play, seeing Francesca's dark fire illuminating the leading role. How wonderful to direct the play, and to feel the two of them working as one to create something of meaning and beauty.

Wonderful—and terrible too. For with such a one there were bound to be quarrels. Not the kind of quarrels Miguel had known with his mother and sisters and the few other women of his acquaintance—quarrels which chiefly stemmed from "how it would look," and "what would people think." But this time, quarrels that stemmed from principle, quarrels that rose from basic attitudes and deep beliefs.

"You *talk* as though you agreed with me," Francesca would cry. "And yet, when it comes to the point, you are as blind and old-fashioned as any one else. You want a woman to be a chattel, to walk meekly by your side, never lifting her eyes to see anyone or anything. You want me to be that—and then you wonder why I say I will not marry you."

For of course Don Miguel had asked her to marry him. He had asked her almost at once, and as the weeks went on, and the months went on, he kept asking—and she kept refusing. "Admit it," she said to him. "For all you talk of my talent as an actress, as soon as we were married you would want to take me off the stage. You would want to hurry back to Madrid and pen me up in a solemn house where I would be Doña Francesca, and only come out to go to Mass. Admit it, admit it!"

Hotly, Miguel would deny this, all the more hotly for knowing in his heart that she was right. That *was* what he wanted. Years of training and tradition were too much for him here. The independence that made her so unique, terrified him. The world was not safe for that kind of independence. She was so beautiful, so unafraid— he could not stand the way the peasants or the merchants ogled her. He wanted her safe, in the kind of proud and gracious setting that fitted such a woman. How he could afford such a setting for her, granting the miracle that she would accept it, was an unanswerable question. But still that was what he wanted, and it infected more and more of his words to her.

"Don't do this, don't do that," he would say, and then bite his tongue as she flung him a taunting look and went on to do exactly as she had intended.

The times between quarrels were still sweet, still heady, but as the months went on, the times between them grew shorter and shorter.

And then, one dreadful morning when Miguel went looking for her in the inn where the whole troupe was staying, he simply could not find her. "Oh, the lady?" questioned the innkeeper, suddenly rousing himself. "She left—late last night. I almost forgot—she left this for you." And he handed Miguel a folded note.

The note explained nothing, really; it said nothing more than what she had been saying to him right along. She loved him, perhaps she would always love him. But he was too strong for her. She was afraid of him. If she stayed, sooner or later he would win, he would make her the kind of woman that he wished—and then, when he

145

had made her so, he would no longer want her, after all. So she was leaving him—before he himself had a chance to change, to leave her instead.

Perhaps she was right. Perhaps in her madness for independence she saw more clearly than could Miguel what their future would have been together. But "too strong?" Never had Miguel felt so weak, so strengthless, as though every source of joy and meaning in his life had vanished.

For a while, he tried to trace her—to find her, bring her back—marry her out of hand. He went about it in a wild, agitated sort of way, quite different from his usual, ordered calm. But it was hopeless; Francesca had left no trace of her flight behind her.

Miguel went through the days in a kind of blind fever, and at night he lay awake for hours in the dark. It seemed to him now that nothing, nothing in his life had ever gone right. He had lost everything he had wanted. He had wanted the chance to fight bravely as a soldier—and he had fought, for a few brief moments only, at Lepanto. At last he had been on the way to promotion and the chance of action—and was captured by the pirates. He had tried to escape, time after time, and had failed always. He had tried to serve his King—in any kind of post—and had failed again. He had found a woman to love at last, a real woman, proud, fiery and beautiful—and now he had lost her too.

Gradually he grew quieter. He moved in a certain detached melancholy. Oh, he still smiled, he still laughed at jests, and made his own; he chuckled, and his face lighted up when laughter rocked through an audience in response to one of his comic scenes on the stage. But then, his face would settle into sadness again. He was himself the Knight of the Mournful Countenance now—as he was to dub Don Quixote one day in the future.

Traveling with the company no longer had its old magic. It was a business. At the close of an evening's efforts, Miguel would count the play's take carefully. If it was not as much as had been expected, he would go about among the players, telling them they were moving on the next morning. In no case were there ever many coins to divide. It was hard to believe that he had actually won a certain amount of prestige for himself in the world of the theater. He knew that here, there, and elsewhere, other companies were performing his plays. Naturally, they gave him no percentage of their

146

earnings. Literary piracy was the usual thing in those days. Miguel himself borrowed as freely from others. The pirated author had only the satisfaction of pleased vanity. The whole business of writing plays had very few satisfactions—except the pleasure of creating them.

Miguel began to wonder a little about writing a book. Whether or not there would be more money in that he did not know. Certainly there would be more fame and prestige; that is, if he were at all successful.

Not long after this, he chanced to be in Madrid briefly. While he was there he met the publisher, Gil Robles. With hardly any preamble, Robles asked Miguel if he would like to write a novel for him. Miguel agreed at once, even though he was not too pleased with the type of novel the publisher wanted. Robles desired a pastoral piece, set in an Arcadian background, with strange adventures and a highly involved plot, in which gods and mortals would intermingle. It was the kind of book of which the public never seemed to tire—a worn-out piece of pastureland, so far as Miguel was concerned. But Robles was so sure Miguel could produce the kind of novel he wanted that he offered him a sizable cash advance.

Very well. It would be a challenge to his literary skill. Miguel rejoined the troupe of actors long enough to say farewell, then returned to Madrid to settle down to writing his first novel.

12

IN WHICH *it is related how our hero writes a book and has a marriage arranged!*

MIGUEL came back to Madrid to write his book because Madrid seemed the only suitable place for an author. In Madrid, where his reputation among theater people was already established, he could write plays as well. And, of course, it was natural in Madrid to return to live in his father's house.

His father's house . . . Actually, it should be called his mother's house, for it was she who set the tone. The male members, welcome and loved though they were, were really only tolerated. Miguel moved into his old room, making it as much as possible his private lair, but outside it, being the considerate man that he was, he did his best to conform to the rules which his mother thought so indispensable. He felt much closer to his father, whose integrity he now saw more clearly than ever. This man had somehow achieved the preservation of his own personality. Of course, he too had had to make concessions, at home as well as to society in general, but if ever there was a doctor devoted to his calling, it was Don Rodrigo. He really cared for his sick ones; but along with the human beings whom he tried to help, he was also the scientist, aiming to learn. Thus, while he did his best to prevent an ulcer, he also watched with utmost interest its continuous growth. When he took a student along (he had a few of these), he might become eloquently enthusiastic about a gorgeous gangrene.

On rare occasions, a colleague would call on Don Rodrigo and take him in the dead of the night to some dark house where, in deepest secrecy, doctors were giving an anatomical lecture. This meant the dissection of a corpse—a thing so strictly forbidden that the doctors who participated felt like criminals. Indeed, it was not easy to gain knowledge, even through books. There were few of

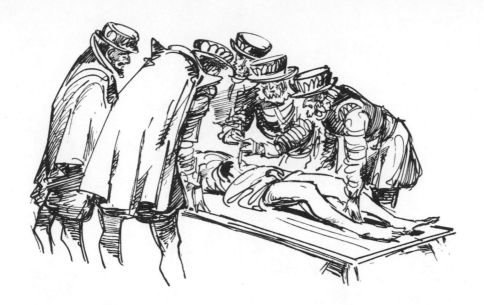

these, and they were expensive and inaccurate. The only work of importance was the anatomical atlas of Vesalius, published a few years before Miguel was born. It is a work rated highly for its clarity and detail, even today, although of course it is medically far from perfect.

Doña Leonora had little admiration for these endeavors of her husband. They seemed to her a waste of time, and she would have preferred it if Don Rodrigo had contented himself with attending the wealthy patients who had no visible ulcers and paid well.

The two men, husband and son, seemed equally strange to poor Doña Leonora; the one, the husband, possessed by his duty, an almost fanatical doctor, disregarding the profitable side of his vocation all but entirely; the other, the son, equally possessed, a writer who had come home merely because he had to sit down somewhere. She feared that Miguel would not stay long, and that any call—be it the stage, or some other duty—would take him away from her, that his vagrant life would begin again. She worried and pondered over how she could make him take root, for in spite of all the ways he had disappointed her, she was strongly attached to him. A marriage for him might be the solution. If she could only find him a wife, marriage would certainly clip his wings.

Actually, she had been looking for a bride for Miguel, with at least half an eye, ever since they had come to Madrid a long time ago. It did not matter if Miguel was near or far; the thought of

finding a worthy mate for him was always in her mind. The bride had to be of nobility—that was a matter of course. Had she looked for a wife among the commoners, she could easily have found a girl with looks, and even wealth, who would have been happy to marry her son—if only for the distinction of becoming a Doña. But Doña Leonora would not consider such a match. However, she did not live completely in the clouds. She realized that, in the eyes of others, her son did not rate so very high. *She* knew what an unusual man he was, simply because he was her son, but she could not deny that he was—and always had been—a fool in all practical matters, and alas, no breadwinner.

But one day she heard of a priest whose niece was living in the country. This young person was said to be exactly the kind of girl she was looking for. The girl on whom she fastened her sights—the victim, one might even call her—was a young creature, nineteen years old. Her name was Catalina de Palacios y Salazar y Vosmediano. Her family, though living the life of farmers, was of quite noble stamp.

Indeed, the Palacios y Salazars were of such unalloyed nobility that they scorned city life. They owned land that was mortgage-free, unlike the big estates of the grandees. Thus Catalina was not forced to accept the first eligible young man who came along. She was pretty, and more important, virtuous. Virtue was in such high esteem that her relatives considered the young Catalina a prize of incalculable value.

The
BRIDE
and
her
FAMILY

Catalina, living on an isolated estate, had hardly ever seen a young man of her standing. As for keeping a girl in seclusion, the Palacios were just as strict as Doña Leonora. It looked almost as if she might be doomed to be a spinster. Thus the Palacios were equally ready to look for a proper match; and when Doña Leonora broached the subject, with the help of the priest, complicated arbitrations began. Such a marriage had to be considered wisely, every point weighed, and every ancient aunt and distant cousin must have her or his pennyworth of advice. Everyone was listened to—except the two main characters—the prospective bride and bridegroom—neither of whom had anything to say, and both of whom were only hazily, if at all, aware of what was going on.

Miguel, busily at work on his book, which he had already outlined, deciding to call it "The Beautiful Galatea," heard his mother

say something about marriage, but she had been saying something about that for years. He did not really think anything serious was going on.

But nothing could have been more serious than the lengthy discussions which were taking place in the yard of the old farmhouse. The Palacios found many faults with Miguel. Doña Leonora had depicted him as a hero who had risked his life for the greater glory of Spain, a man of letters who had made a reputation as a playwright; a generous man, and one who would be good to the girl Catalina. In the opinion of the Palacios, however, he was crippled, unfit for work; a vagabond who had spent most of life, heaven knew where, a spendthrift and a poor provider. They counted on their fingers what his burdens would be if he took a wife: the wife herself, a mother, two sisters—and in the future they hoped for children! The father was getting old, he could not be of help for much longer. How would Miguel ever manage to support this host of women? But— Catalina was getting on in years, almost twenty! In her village there were no suitors. Cash had never come into the hands of the Palacios —like genuine farmers, they invested in land, so there was no dowry. Thus it went, back and forth, until finally it was obvious to Doña Leonora that it was time to produce Miguel himself—perhaps he would be the trump card.

Miguel felt a shock of cold dismay when he realized his mother *was* serious about marriage this time, and that things had actually progressed to the point where he was supposed to meet the prospective bride. "No!" he shouted loudly, when his mother told him of the plans for meeting. ("Marry me," he had said over and over to Francesca—but Francesca was gone, and he was finished with all thoughts of both love and marriage.) Doña Leonora was insistent. It was a man's duty to marry and have a family. Did he not want children to carry on his name? A wife to look after him when his mother was gone? On and on she talked, and Miguel's first wild resistance began to change to weariness and a desire to have his mother quiet at any cost. Many of the things she said were true. A man was supposed to marry and have children. Perhaps—perhaps this girl, young as she was, might bring back a little of the warmth that had vanished with Francesca. Perhaps . . . "Oh, all right," he said at last. "All right." And his mother left the room triumphantly, to see about arranging a time for the Palacios to meet her son.

153

Miguel made a very favorable impression on the Palacios. He was a man of the world, a nobleman—you could see that the moment he entered the room; good-looking, too, and Catalina, who had an opportunity to observe him from behind a curtain (Miguel must not see her yet)—Catalina was all blushes and excitement, for here was a man, a real man—and all for her. It was probably Catalina who pushed the balance in Miguel's favor. And after all, what had the Palacios to lose?

After they had agreed to the match, there came the more important question of the dowry. Again the haggling took its course, and now the discussions were extremely spirited. Tenaciously, the farmers held to their own, yielding practically nothing, and every so often they discovered that they could not bear to part with their darling after all. The women wept, the men sat with gloomy faces. All this was a ritual. In the end the contract was drawn up, signed and sealed. And this is what Catalina was to bring to her new home: seven grape plants of good wine, a number of chickens, some silver spoons, and a skillet. The grapevines remained in the earth anyway, chickens were dispensable, but to part with silver spoons and a skillet—this was a real sacrifice!

After this, Miguel himself was finally allowed to see Catalina. He went hesitantly, with old memories and miseries rising afresh in his heart. He had no wish to involve himself again in all those aching emotions. He had no right to offer an innocent young girl a heart already worn out and cold. But then he saw her young, heart-shaped face behind the bars of the first-floor window of the farm. There she sat, so primly, her duenna beside her (a duenna being an elderly person of supposedly high morals whose presence would prevent any untoward or honest remarks at all)—and she was so very young, such an eager, trusting child, that Miguel could not help but be gentle and kind to her. He whispered a few pleasant remarks, recited a poem he had written for her (in desperate haste, at the last minute, with his mother urging him on to the farmhouse)—and that was their meeting. He went away quietly, quite calm now about marrying this young person. After all, she was attractive; pretty hands, a white skin, an agreeable manner—why should he object?

A marriage once had a different meaning from that of today. Where we think of the happiness of two persons as an important factor, this was neither mentioned nor considered. A marriage was, first of all, an alliance of two clans, a strengthening of common interests, a pursuit of power. The expected children would eventually make the two clans into one unit. This concept still exists among royalty, and a few leading families, though the human factor more and more thwarts careful planning and scheming. In the days of Don Miguel de Cervantes, however, love was a privilege of the poor, who were not fettered and fenced by interests and possessions.

Still, when it came time for the wedding day, the *appearance* of mirth and bliss were obligatory. Everyone knew very well why these two were getting married; still, at the moment of ceremony, the fiction that they married for love was necessary to everyone. The fictions men live by—there it was again for Miguel, at his own wedding feast now, where, to any strange observer, it would seem the two happiest mortals in the world were being joined together. Was it reality because all men said so, was it reality because books and poems and plays all praised this day as the apex of a man's life? Or was reality itself only illusion—and if so—then what was illusion?

Whatever his secret thoughts, Miguel moved through the ceremonies of the wedding celebration, which lasted for several days, with patience and dutiful smiles. He managed to be friendly with the many old hags who had become his in-laws, and he won friends among the men, astonishing them with his good knowledge of the farmers' problems. When he left, after the last wine was drunk, all of the Palacios had the impression that it was a very good match, after all.

So Miguel took his young wife back to the house in Madrid, and shy little Catalina, who had never been outside her native village, entered into her new life. So far as Catalina was concerned, her husband was a wonderful man, close to her image of the ideal husband. She hoped to prove herself a helpful, capable, level-headed wife; she hoped to be up to the household duties and abilities that were expected of a woman.

Unfortunately, in all this Catalina reckoned without her redoubtable mother-in-law. Although Doña Leonora had worked hard for this match, she still considered Catalina far beneath her son. After a ceremonial welcome to the young wife, Doña Leonora was ready to shove her into a corner and forget her. As for Andrea and Luisa, now that their new sister-in-law was actually in the house, they too had their reservations about her. Andrea despised Catalina's prettiness,

and considered her both conceited and sinful. Luisa, on the other hand, thought she had never seen such idiotic and childlike innocence on the face of the earth.

Hopefully, Catalina offered to cook, and was given to understand there was much she needed to learn before she could prepare an *olla podrida* the way Miguel liked it. Hopefully, she offered to wash, and heard sarcastic remarks about her white hands. She offered to mend or sew, and was given things she could not do, and consequently was scorned. Jealously, the three women of the Cervantes family guarded their domestic realm against the newcomer. Spoons, chickens, grapes and a skillet! Ha! A well-shaped little nose and a pair of attractive eyes could hardly make up for such a dowry. True, one day she might bring a son into the world, an heir, but at the moment she was just one burden more.

As for Miguel himself, when he saw how things were going for her, he consoled her and fondled her. She was a sweet child. He wished he could give her more. Trying to think of some way to please or entertain her, he read her chapters from "The Beautiful Galatea." Catalina was both embarrassed by the honor, and flattered by what she heard. She fancied that she herself was the heroine of the book, and it gave her some badly needed confidence. Actually, so long as she was near Miguel, none of the other difficulties of her new life troubled her at all. Catalina loved Miguel. He was the first and only person who treated her with consideration, and he had freed her from that horde of old people at the farm. He was kind, patient and understanding; he was adventurous and gay and could make her laugh as she never had laughed before with his stories. No, really, she had nothing to complain of, so long as Miguel was near.

So the days went on, and Catalina gradually began to be accepted as a member of the Cervantes y Saavedra family. Miguel's work with his book continued. And then, finally, it was finished, and delivered to the publisher. And instead of feeling pleased or elated, Miguel daily felt his spirits grow heavier.

The more Catalina was accepted by the women of his family, the more remote she seemed to him. What had he been thinking of when he consented to marry? Perhaps he had been so involved with his book that he was not thinking at all. But now that the book was finished, it was all perfectly clear. He had no business being married, no sympathy for domestic life in the least. He thought of Francesca and his heart twisted. Perhaps she had known him better than he knew himself—thinking he wanted marriage, and then when he had it, feeling trapped and hounded by the tyranny of its routine.

It did not improve his spirits at all when "The Beautiful Galatea" turned out to be a success. He went to the cafés, to find that his friends were taking it very seriously, and he was aggravated almost beyond bearing. Could they not see? It was not his book. Could they not understand it was a literary exercise which had been forced on

him? True, he had executed it better than he had anticipated; but it was, after all, just one more pastoral novel, one more book with an unreal setting and a plot so involved it left the reader baffled. Yes, the book did have some fantasy and wit, it was written in nobler language than most of such books, but it contained almost nothing of himself.

When Gil Robles, the publisher, urged Miguel to write a sequel, Miguel could not even pretend an interest.

Neither Robles nor his friends seemed to understand his point of view. And now that the proof was at hand that Miguel could earn money, all of his family—father, mother, sisters and wife—joined in a chorus urging him to write.

What was to be done? He was torn between the need to make some money and this terrible reluctance to put all his intelligence to work on another such exercise. Once he had turned from the impossibility of finding a government post to the possibility of writing. Now that he had written, and found the taste of success flat and unprofitable, he played again with the idea of re-entering the army or finding some post with the government. It was not really so absurd to think of it right now. He had reason to believe that something suitable to his age and capacities might be obtainable.

A new spirit was perceptible in the land, a throbbing undercurrent of activity. Some of the details were public knowledge, some were only to be guessed at. The news was spreading, though, that Spain was building a great fleet to launch against England.

13

WHICH TELLS *of the strained relations between Spain and England, and how they profited Don Miguel!*

EVERYWHERE in Madrid, everywhere in Spain, the fury against England had been growing. There were many reasons for this anger, but as Miguel heard men talking in the streets, and in the cafés of Madrid, it was Elizabeth of England on whom the fiercest blame was centered.

Elizabeth! Had there ever been such a headstrong queen? She said of herself that she "had the frail body of a woman, but the brains and stomach of a man." Certainly all her actions confirmed her own judgment. Chiefly, of course, in Catholic Spain, it was her activity against the One True Church which made men look on her as a monster.

Before this daughter of Henry VIII and Anne Boleyn had come to the throne, England had swayed back and forth between Catholicism and Protestantism. For a little while in the 1550's, Spain's own Philip II had been married to Mary, an older daughter of Henry. Then Catholicism had triumphed in England. Philip had seen to that, cleaning out Protestantism all over the country and earning for his Queen the grim title, "Bloody Mary." She was the one who had to take responsibility for her husband's orders. But then, after only four years of marriage, Mary had died, and Philip had seen with dismay that his power to defend the faith in England died with her. Quickly, he had proposed marriage to the new Queen, Elizabeth, but Elizabeth had turned him down. "Thank God," was all men could say now, as they viewed the "monster's" ever-increasing hostility to the Church.

In the beginning of her reign, Elizabeth made a compromise between the two faiths. She preserved many of the Protestant reforms her father had introduced. The Pope had no influence in England,

and the King, or Queen, of the realm was supreme head of the Church of England. And even though the English doctrine was still very close, in essence, to the Catholic doctrine, Protestants were no longer persecuted when Elizabeth took over.

This alone was disturbing enough to Philip II, the self-appointed exterminator of Protestants. But then, as the years went on, Elizabeth grew harsher and harsher towards the Catholics, and her policy here, there and everywhere turned out to be aid for the Protestants against the Catholics.

Spain had ruled the Netherlands since the days when it came into possession of those lowlands through the House of Hapsburg. But the Protestants had been in rebellion there for a long time now, requiring the constant attention of Spanish armies. Miguel's brother Rodrigo was still fighting there, as he had been years before.

And now, who was helping the Dutch maintain this endless revolt? Elizabeth! She claimed England was sending the Netherlands arms and supplies only in the nature of business, but what Spaniard would believe that!

Nor was this all. On the high seas, Elizabeth's ships chased and looted Spanish frigates as they returned from Mexico loaded with treasure. The captains who commanded the ships—men like Drake, Raleigh and Hawkins—were called pirates the world over, but in England, the Queen gave them titles and rewarded them with a share of the loot.

Other adventurous Englishmen were landing in unknown territories in North America, laying claim to these lands—and in whose name? Elizabeth's!

Oh, she was a threat everywhere! And then, when it seemed she must surely have reached the limits of even her ingenuity in tormenting Spain, she ordered the execution of Mary Stuart of Scotland. And Mary was a Catholic.

Any political reasons Elizabeth might have had for this act were

completely ignored in **Spain. Mary had** been killed for her faith, and every Spaniard reacted **with as** much anguish as if his own sister had gone to her death.

While the fury and outrage at what was termed murder were **still** burning high, Sir Francis Drake sailed into the harbor of Cadiz, where Spain's main fleet for the American trade was anchored. There, in broad daylight, Drake burned and sank more than half of the ships. Then, before the gunners on the ramparts had time **to right** their cannons, the vessels of Drake had turned about **and were** out on the high seas again.

It was scarcely any wonder that all Spain was aflame with **fury** —hardly any wonder that everywhere Miguel heard heated **talk about** a vast expedition to go forth to punish these vile, heretical **English.**

Everywhere in Spain now, the forges worked day and night, **the** armorers hammered away at breastplates and helmets, and wharves were piled high with guns and ammunition. Everyone knew at **least** part of Philip's plan. He was building a great fleet, an Armada, which would be the strongest in all history—and with this fleet he was going to send his armies to England, to wrest that country from Elizabeth's grasp.

Obviously, with such plans afoot, with such activity and excitement all over Spain, there was a place for Miguel somewhere in the service of his King. He had just begun again on the old round of interviews, petitions and pleas, when his father died.

Don Rodrigo had lived to be well over seventy. His death was not unexpected, but it left Miguel feeling very abandoned and forlorn. These two men had understood and respected each other. They had the same outlook on life—and they had been brothers-in-arms against the host of women. It was not that either of them quarreled with any of the women individually, but as a group, the women were like a hostile camp.

Now, with his father dead and the house in mourning, Miguel felt more and more that the women had completely taken over—that there was no room for him there at all, except as the object of their endless fussing and clucking attention. His mother was constantly bringing him medical concoctions, concerning herself with his health. Andrea was constantly watching over his spiritual life, praying for him, urging him to Mass and confession. As for Catalina, the poor little child-wife, it was against her that Miguel felt his irritation rise highest, though actually, she did the least to deserve it. All she did was follow about after him whenever he was in the house, hoping to serve him some way, to bring him something, do something for him. That was all, except for her constant questions about when he was going to write another novel—or play or poem —about her. In his heart, Miguel hated himself for his irritation, but there it was, daily growing, threatening to devour him. Truly, he told himself, Catalina would be happier if he were not around all the time to agitate her into these states of unfulfilment. She could join ranks with the other women—he had seen her alone with them, and knew she had learned to be happier then than she really was with him.

So he argued with himself, and then came the opportunity for which he had been waiting—an opportunity that seemed heaven-sent. He was offered a post that would solve everything—take him away from the house for an extended period, and yet enable him to provide for his wife and the other women adequately. Along with all that, it was a post with real prestige at last, a post that gave him an opportunity to use all his intelligence and judgment in the service of his King and country. He was appointed a Quartermaster, or deputy purveyor to the fleet, with the task of helping to requisition supplies and provisions for the fast-building Armada.

Catalina wept at his departure. All the women wept. But somehow Miguel guessed that for all their tears, they were secretly as relieved as he at the parting. No longer would they have to tiptoe

around while he was in the house supposedly writing, no longer would they have to break off their gossiping or their quarreling at his arrivals, no longer would all their lives have to circle and bypass the rocklike obstacle of his presence. The house could become a calm pond of femininity without him.

And he—he could enter again into the world of men, the world that was more appropriate to someone who had always thought of himself as a soldier. On his doublet now, he bore the King's coat-of-arms, and the men who assisted him were all soldiers.

It was his task to ride about the countryside, followed by a provisions wagon and a handful of soldiers, servants and horsemen, requisitioning supplies from rich and poor everywhere. He must see to it that the business of obtaining these supplies went smoothly, and without undue severity. On the other hand, he must not allow anyone to cheat him—or the King.

It was not an easy job. Wherever he appeared, he was unwelcome. Doors were slammed, windows shut tight in his face. Even when this did not literally occur, the hostility was apparent in the faces and reactions of those he visited. Still, with simple eloquence, he generally managed to convince the stiff-necked barons, the stingy peasants, and the always-worried widows, that if they handed over a jar of oil they would not necessarily starve, and it was right and necessary for them to make some sacrifice for the sake of Spain's victory.

Miguel tried hard to make sure his demands were never unreasonable, and did not go beyond any individual's ability to give. And when the people he visited realized he was indeed fair-minded and had a real understanding of their troubles, their hearts opened and smiles appeared on their faces. Grudgingly at first, but then with un-

stinting hands, they gave their contributions. Reluctantly, they had
permitted him to ride into their courtyards—but he took with him
their blessing when he departed. Soon the rumor spread that this
Don Miguel was quite different from the other officials engaged in
requisitioning, and though everyone still met him with protestations
of poverty, he himself was no longer regarded as an enemy.

Now Miguel's area of operations was widened. It was extended to
include the hills of the Sierra Morena and adjacent areas in southern
Spain. He was pleased by this evidence of his success and began to
feel that the bad luck which had dogged him so often through his
life was ending at last. And then bad luck struck again!

His travels through the new territory brought him now to a monastery in Ecija where he was to levy more provisions for the Crown.
But here, in the monastery, he met resistance. Abbot and monk de-
fied him with ludicrous lamentations. They refused to show him the
monastery larders, and cursed him as though he were the Antichrist.
All Miguel's eloquence was expended in vain, so that finally, without further ado, he bade his soldiers enter the cellar and storerooms
and haul out what seemed like a fair proportion of provisions. The
monks stood about, cursing and lamenting, and when Miguel rode
away, dire threats and maledictions followed him.

Several days later, he and his train rode into Seville where they
were scheduled to unload this consignment of supplies. Almost at
once Miguel was sought out by a messenger with a dreadful summons. He was ordered to appear before the Inquisition!

At this moment, he had no idea why he was being summoned—

no idea what the charge was against him. The paper did not say. His mind groped back dizzily to the monastery he had visited, the supplies he had taken under protest. Could that be the reason? He had not taken much from the monastery, less even than would have been fair as a contribution from such a well-stocked cellar. But that would make no difference. One never knew what trivial thing the Inquisition might consider worthy of the gravest punishment. One never knew what long-forgotten, hardly realized offense might suddenly have come to its attention, either.

Miguel began to feel cold, despite the hot sunshine that beat down on him as he stood, transfixed, the summons still in his hand. Memories were sweeping back upon him from earliest childhood now, long-forgotten, deep-buried sounds and smells—the moaning and praying of men sentenced to the *auto-da-fés*—the smell . . . the smell of burned hair. He shuddered. Just once he had been locked in a crowd, gathered to witness a public burning, and the howling of the mob echoed again in his ears, the singing of the monks, the tolling of the bells, the wild screams of the victims.

Miguel clenched the message in his hand and turned swiftly on his heel to enter the inn. He would keep himself under control, he would not give way to panic before this summons. But it was easier to say this to himself than to banish the terror that surrounded every aspect of the Inquisition. All his life he had heard stories, and they came back to him now in flashing, terrifying scenes. In Zaragoza they had burned a witch—she was an eight-year-old girl. Somewhere else, a man had not crossed himself when the Angelus sounded. This had been sufficient reason to order him burned alive, and he—Don Miguel de Cervantes—thought that his invasion of the monastery was a *trivial* thing. One man was condemned for befriending a Jew; there was another who had not fasted on Friday. Everyone was guilty, sometime or another, of dozens of the offenses for which the Inquisition had condemned men to death. The only thing that protected anyone was the fact that there was no one who disliked him enough to report him.

Once an offense was reported, doom of one kind or another was on its way. The Inquisition investigated every case that was reported. Thousands of monks worked on tens of thousands of cases. The dungeons were crowded with men and women in abject despair, left there to rot until their cases were settled.

Miguel got up and left the inn—to walk the streets, fleeing his own fear. The Inquisition never admitted mistakes. Whoever appeared before it was already condemned. The only issue to be decided was the nature of the punishment. He remembered the years in Rome, when for the first time in his life he had been away from the spell of the Spanish Inquisition long enough to see it in some perspective. He remembered the Romans shaking their heads over the extravagance of the Spanish punishments—the San Benitos—the confiscations of property—the burnings—the burnings. But what good did it do to remember *Rome's* attitude now? He was in Spain, where the Inquisition was all-powerful, and he was in its grip.

When Miguel was led before the tribunal, he stood alone against this dread authority. He saw human beings, but they were not individuals; they were officials of the impersonal power whose laws he was alleged to have violated. He stood on his feet, but felt no solid ground beneath him. He looked at faces, but what he saw meant nothing to him. The zealous Dominicans who sat opposite him had nothing for or against him personally. He was defenseless and naked against them.

He was not afraid of the day on which he would be called upon

to answer to a Higher Power. God was goodness and mercy. There was not even any reason for him to make confession: God knew everything. But facing this wall of fanatical monks, self-appointed judges over everything and everyone, he shuddered.

Then the indictment was read, in Latin and in Spanish. He let out his breath. He was not accused of having consorted with witches or committing acts of heresy. It *was* the Ecija affair, the matter involving the monastery from which he had seized provisions. Now, it seemed, he should have known that monasteries were exempt from such levies. He did not know it, he answered. "Indeed," replied the judges. Then it would still seem he had shown an unChristian spirit in not respecting the protests of the monks and honoring the sanctity of the monastery of his own accord. Miguel bowed his head, admitting the charge and waiting for the punishment.

He could hardly believe his ears. He was being given the lightest sentence of all—a warning. Of course the warning carried with it a sentence of excommunication for a period of several months. For a

faithful Catholic, it was hard indeed to be denied all the comforts, privileges and blessings of the Church for any length of time. Still, he had his life, he had his freedom—he even had his job still.

He left the Tribunal, almost light-headed in his relief, and went back to his travels on the roads of Andalusia, gathering wagonload after wagonload of provisions for the Armada.

In the late spring of 1588, Miguel heard that the fleet was ready at last. One part of it consisted of huge galleons, larger than any previously seen on the water. The bulk of it, however, was made up of heavy galleys. The King, *El Prudente,* the Cautious One, himself had dubbed it Invincible.

The plan called for the Invincible Armada to sail for England with a battle-seasoned army which would be landed there to fight on English soil. In the Lowlands, a second contingent of the Spanish army stood ready. Both forces together were considered unbeatable by the prevailing standards. Certainly the English, who had nothing to send against them but a force of poorly armed burghers, did not have a chance. Elizabeth was going to be punished! Elizabeth was going to be crushed!

Miguel lingered in Seville now, eager for news. And then came word of a tragedy. On the very eve of the Armada's sailing, the commanding admiral, the Marquis of Santa Cruz, had died unexpectedly. One week, two weeks, three, dragged by in arguments over whom to appoint as his successor. Finally, the new commander-in-chief was chosen—a man who was not a naval type at all, but simply a man of high rank who had been chosen to avoid feuds between a group of equally qualified candidates.

At last, the fleet was leaving the harbor! Off it sailed, all Spain's prayers with it. And then, a second disaster struck. The vessels, encountering a terrible storm, were forced to turn back and seek haven at La Coruna. The storm had caused much damage to the ships. It was several weeks before the news went around Seville that the Armada had finally sailed again.

It was July by now. The hot summer settled down, and with the heat there was silence. Miguel and his companions sat in the cafés and wondered, and speculated and hoped, and heard nothing. To be sure, couriers, spurring their horses to exhaustion, brought back detailed reports to the King from far up Europe's coast, but no one in the country at large had any idea what was in those reports.

Then, gradually, the news began to trickle forth. The information was sparse and vague, but soon it was plain that nothing had turned out as planned. Miguel began to feel very uneasy. A good many of his more boisterous and over-confident acquaintances began to grow quieter. Finally they sank into complete silence. Weeks passed, yet the Church ordered no bells pealed for victory. Instead, Masses were held for those who had died at sea. The autumn storms raged in the Bay of Biscay, and still the population waited, clinging desperately to the possibility of some miracle. Then the ships returned. In small groups they limped into ports. The people waited for the rest of the ships, but these did not come back.

"What happened?" Miguel cried now, along with all of Spain, and at last the details of the catastrophe started to come clear. Bad luck, adverse weather and underestimation of the foe had all combined to bring on disaster.

An additional factor had been the strategy. The Spaniards had intended to ship an army across the sea, to fight a land battle. Even when hostile ships came abreast, the plan was still to use the decks as battlegrounds and let the soldiers fight. Spain had no interest in, nor awareness of, the sailor's role in warfare. The soldier was glorified, the sailor despised as a man who was simply necessary to get the soldier to his destination.

The English, it seemed, had different ideas. Their ships were manned with sailors, not soldiers. Their ships were smaller than the Spanish, and more maneuverable. The British had a greater skill in sailing, too. There had been bad weather, true, but bad weather hits both parties. There had been bad luck, but also good luck for the Spaniards, else not one ship would have escaped. And there had been an amazing underestimation of the British spirit and fighting power.

Listening to all the talk, Miguel's mind kept going back to his one unforgettable experience in warfare, the Battle of Lepanto. The Spaniards had fought then, as they fought this time. What was wrong? Once again, he was too much part of his own time to know that the Battle of Lepanto had been the last major naval engagement in the old style—using the ships to bring soldiers to their destination—and then—be it on deck or on land—letting the soldiers fight it out the land army way. The great battle that had finally taken place in the English Channel between the Armada and the British fleet had been the first sea battle in modern style, using ships as ships, not as platforms, relying on precision firing and maneuver and speed.

The somber details went on. The Spanish ships could never get close enough to the shores of England to attempt a landing. The fleet was scattered, the squadrons broken up. As to the waiting army on Dutch soil, it needed ships too, and it was locked in the estuary of a river. Not a single soldier got off.

Scattered away from England, the Spaniards tried to reassemble, but the British units pressed hard on every side. This, plus adverse winds, finally drove the Armada into the North Sea. Still fleeing the determined English, the Spaniards had to round the British Isles

up around Scotland, and try to sail south again through the Irish Sea. Bad water and rotting meat caused all sorts of diseases to develop. Soldiers and sailors died of typhus and cholera. Waves swept many overboard, and high winds plunged crewmen from the yardarms as they reefed the sails. Half of the ships managed to get back safely, but only a tiny fraction of their crews was still in sound health. Wounded and ill, they crept or were carried into barracks and hospitals to try to recover. "The scars a soldier bears are stars . . ." The stars were clustered thick in Spain these days—and to those who could read them, (but they were few)—they spelled the end of Spain's glory, the end of Spanish control of the seas, the end of the rule in the Netherlands, the end of Spain's world domination.

All this was not clear to Miguel, nor to his friends and acquaintances either. One thing *was* clear, however, and they sat heavily around the tables is the cafés, trying to accept it. The Invincible Armada had been destroyed. For all their efforts, all their hopes, all their prayers, the Invincible had been conquered, and was no more.

Still—from every belfry the church bells tolled the *Te Deum*, the prayer of thanksgiving. There was no resentment against God, and the King knelt many hours in prayer.

Obviously, there was no longer any need for quartermasters to supply provisions to a fleet or an army. But Miguel was now on the official list and remained employed. He continued to draw up petitions for one or another of the many government posts available.

He wondered if it might be possible to obtain a sinecure in the West Indies, Mexico or Peru. The names had a magic sound of color and richness to them. But this dream came to nothing.

What he did receive was an appointment as a tax collector, which was certainly no sinecure, and for a time his headquarters remained in Seville.

14

IN WHICH *our hero visits the rich and the poor,*
seeking their money—and winds up in jail!

IN SEVILLE there was a great hostelry, a "grand hotel" in today's
terms, which belonged to a friend of Miguel's, a former actor he
had known in the theater days. This man had chosen the more profitable and comfortable calling of an innkeeper, leaving the battle for
artistic ideals in the hands of younger enthusiasts. This friend now
offered Don Miguel a small attic room in his inn for a lodging place
in Seville. It was a tiny cubbyhole at best, but it gave Miguel a full
view of the courtyard below, as well as a magnificent sweep of the
distant Sierras.

At that time, travelers were flocking to Seville from every country;
merchants, officials, priests, important diplomats, professors, and
doctors, and, of course, all sorts of dubious and questionable characters who made a point of stopping at this fine inn so as to enhance
their reputations.

Miguel knew many of them from the corridors and antechambers
of the palace at Madrid. He knew them all, actually; if they were not
the identical persons, they were unmistakably the same types, among
them grandees with resounding titles, or high-ranking ecclesiastics.
He looked down at them in the courtyard from his little room up
under the eaves, and a wry smile curled his lips. How differently
they behaved here than at court! In Madrid, they had strutted
elegantly about, displaying only two facial attitudes to the world:
to their inferiors, an expression of blatant arrogance—to the others,
an ever-present smirk which they proffered as a friendly smile.
Now these individuals alighted from their coaches or horses after
a long, wearisome journey and revealed another self entirely. Most
of them were exhausted and their finery was in a sorry state.

Their collars were dirty and limp, their feathers had to be curled anew. Their faces were sullen, imperious, aloof; or timid, uncertain, distrustful. The very way in which they stretched their limbs after the trying journey, the way they requested lodging or treated the servants hurrying past, revealed much about their characters.

Up at his garret window, Miguel smiled, and then the smile faded, and he drifted into a fit of musing. He too had several selves, the self who faced the peasants of Andalusia, when he was collecting provisions for the Armada—a sympathetic, everyday, humble self, like the men he met. It was another Don Miguel entirely whom his wife and mother and sister knew—still another Don Miguel who had directed a troupe of traveling actors—and yet another one who had wildly and desperately loved a certain dark-haired beauty. Which was the real Don Miguel? Was there one of all these varied men, who was the essence of what he truly felt himself to be? What was the *essence* of those men he watched below? Was their essence what they believed in? He shook his head and gave it up.

Sometimes, when he was downstairs in the inn, he recognized some of the travelers by sight. They were men he had spoken to in Madrid. He felt a sudden urge to greet these persons. And then, he swiftly downed the impulse. Imperceptibly, a gulf had formed be-

tween him and the other men, and there was no bridging the gulf. He was content and proud to be in the King's service. But he also realized that a tax collector in Andalusia and a grandee had nothing in common, save an allegiance to that King.

Again, he would have to smile, remembering his mother, Doña Leonora, and the need she would have felt for him to be on equal terms with these nobles. It was true, it was part of one kind of reality, that he was born to a noble family, even as they. It was true, too, that not only because of birth, but because of experience, and knowledge, he could have filled the posts of many of them as well as they did. According to his mother's creed, he should then have acted as though he were one of them. But what they believed in and what he believed in were different things. He could not pretend that nobility was more important than honest service. He could not even pretend he wanted their lives more than his own.

Roaming through the rugged mountains of Andalusia, he deeply enjoyed the manly, soldierly life he led—he was a soldier still. He had an eye for the majestic landscapes and he did not mind the hardships caused by the fierceness of the elements.

His work was hard, without regular hours, or clearly defined duties. He was responsible for collecting all back taxes—how he did it was his own affair. No one looked after him; he looked after others, performing his duties conscientiously and in all fairness.

Sometimes he sat in the saddle an entire day without sighting a farmhouse. He rode over the red earth of the parched countryside, past ruins of Morisco settlements, where Don Juan's war of extermination had been so merciless that even now, twenty years later, no one wanted to live there. The woods and groves were bare of foliage because the wells which had watered them had been covered over. Yellow broom was the only vegetation that still grew in the débris of the ruined houses. When Miguel did finally reach his goal, usually some desolate farmhouse, he was sure to be unwelcome. The very dogs were suspicious, sullenly growling and glowering. Doors and windows remained bolted, and signs of life appeared only after loud shouting and pounding on the door. Nevertheless, with no inn for miles around, Miguel frequently had to ask the occupants of these hostile houses for room and board. He was a soldier still, but even so, he preferred a room with a bed to sleeping in the open fields or in his cramped wagon.

But once Miguel was in the house and talking with his hosts, how quickly the mood changed! Hardly were the food and wine served him in an unfriendly manner, when, with a few well-chosen words, he caused his hosts to prick up their ears. Then these dour peasants found that beneath the cloak with the King's coat-of-arms was a second human being, a warmer, more human individual than they had ever encountered.

These men of the sierras and the plains, who worked the soil with their bare hands to grub food, and who knew nothing but hardship, enjoying at best one day of pleasure a year, were hungry for news of the outside world. And this was something Miguel knew how to tell. The weariness of his day's traveling fell from him like a cloak. Sparks lighted in his eyes, and his entire being quickened to new life.

He told them the news of Seville, the news from Madrid, and,

one thing leading to another, there was no end to his stories. All the talent for mimicry which had first come to flower in the long-ago days in Algiers was part of him now. He told of a storm, and the storm was in the house. He spoke of a desert, and his listeners reached for their wine to relieve their parched throats. All his years in the theater were part of him too. One moment he was a beggar, then a grandee, then a prince. His listeners laughed, and gasped, and sighed, and the farmer, long since forgetting his taxes, beckoned to the maidservant for a second tankard of wine for the table.

But for all the stories he told, Miguel was still a good listener, and there was no end to the things he learned in these years from the people of Andalusia. Many a farmer's wife gazed at her husband, whom she thought she knew so well, and saw him as a stranger. To her amazement, she learned that this dull clod, her husband, could also think and feel—and talk—to this curious tax collector.

Often, when the servants had stretched out on the floor and fallen asleep, and darkness and wine had brought the waking ones closer together, the conversation would turn to personal matters. The farmer would sigh and recall the good old days—and then the subject of the Moriscos would come up. In vain the wife, with raised eyebrows, would warn her husband to be careful, and rapidly make

the sign of the Cross, visible proof she was a devout Catholic. Still, there was no denying it—the Moriscos had been a boon to the country and had never done harm to anyone.

Miguel would nod, and speak of the wonders of the Moorish buildings in faraway Algiers. He had seen them. He had lived in them. Even more reassured, the farmer would continue. How skillful the Moriscos had been, how everything had blossomed at their touch! Twenty years before, the bleak, rocky wasteland in which the peasant and his wife now lived had been a veritable paradise. Where the earth now lay parched with drought, swift little streams had coursed. They had such an abundance of water that springs had been tapped solely to cool the air and afford pleasure to their eyes. Huge shade trees had grown where now the red earth refused to bear a single stalk of grain. Then had come the accursed war. Then had come Don Juan of Austria.

The peasant still remembered how as a youth he had learned from Moorish gardeners how to nurture young shoots, graft fruits, protect weak plants and straighten crooked ones. What use were these skills to him now? He was lucky to possess a couple of sheep for shearing and a few olive trees. To water the trees he had to drag a bucket from a well many miles away. Did the King know about this misery and poverty? Evidently not; otherwise, how could he tolerate such deplorable conditions?

Other days Miguel's duties took him into the high plateaus which were first of all sheep-grazing country, and where he was equally unwelcome. Here he visited, not farmers, but noblemen. To these men, Miguel would make known his own social station, and adopt a more formal and ceremonious tone. Two men of noble birth were

179

meeting on equal footing. What if the purpose of the visit were a regrettable one—it was still a social visit! In such a house, business matters were deferred until the following day. The men who accompanied Miguel were given accommodations in the servants' quarters, he himself was presented to the lady of the house and invited to dinner. Later, the men played chess, and drank a glass of better wine, and soon the lord of the manor was talking . . .

He was a nobleman, living in a musty old structure which was called a castle by indulgence only. His social contacts were the priests or a few aristocrats, living a day's journey away, and like himself, vegetating in decay. His son, his hope and pride, was gone —gone to the New World. His daughter spent interminable hours at her embroidery frame, dreaming of what she was missing. The family was too poor to enter her in a convent. Her father and his few friends were the only males she ever saw. . . . What had happened? the nobleman suddenly cried. Thirty years ago this had been a great estate. On the surrounding hills over a hundred thousand sheep had grazed, yielding the finest wool. Countless hands had combed, spun and woven. Now all the looms were silent. Of all the sheep, less than twelve thousand remained, and they brought no income. Formerly, dealers had pled with him for his wool. Now he had to look for someone to take it off his hands. Of course, prices were higher now, but the money meant less. Gold was rarely to be seen, silver was counterfeited, even the copper was not genuine. In short, within a generation, the nobleman had become a beggar, and he was not alone. It was the same with many other fine old families in the region. Did the King know all this? Surely he knew. The story was repeated to him daily. And what was his answer? Taxes, more taxes, nothing but taxes . . .

Other times, Miguel's way took him into the small towns, to the tradesmen, the innkeepers, the coopers and wheelwrights. Everywhere he heard the same song. Where was the gold from Mexico? Why was everyone poor? The law was the only profession that prospered now, so many people were suing each other. And the clergy prospered too, sure of its tithe.

So Miguel went about Andalusia and met its people and heard their stories, learned the rhythm of their lives and their language. So he came to know the Spain that lived behind the ceremonial manners in Madrid and Seville, the Spain of the people who tilled its soil and kept its heart beating.

Miguel spent many years in this fashion, not always in Andalusia, but sometimes in Castille too, or Lèon, or La Mancha. *La Mancha.* It was a name he was one day to make so famous that it echoed around the world; for, of all the provinces in Spain, he chose La Mancha as the home for his very ingenious knight, Don Quixote. Was there something special about La Mancha that made its name so linger in his mind? Not really. In La Mancha there was the same poverty he found every place. There were the same complaints. But beyond the complaining, there were the same people when he probed beneath the surface—anxious, hopeful, wondering and worried about the future.

As the years went on, Miguel reached a point where he knew how an interview would turn out before he began asking questions. In one case, a man would assume a thoughtful air and effusively pour out his heart—yet it was all a transparent fraud. Another would smile uncomfortably, and stammer helplessly, yet Miguel knew that really he could not pay. Often an entire family would huddle together and beg for mercy on bended knees, sobbing piteously, as though he were an executioner. But there were also men of dignity who cooperated with him in the search for an equitable solution of their difficulties.

With the years, Miguel had worked out his own method for resolving problems. It was the spirit of the law, not the letter, which he tried to enforce. And over and over he had found that he could rely on his judgment when he trusted a man.

And then, at last, came the time when his trust was misplaced. There was a merchant who had sworn up and down he would pay the following day. Miguel had believed him. Not only that, but because that evening was his regular evening for bringing his books up to date, he entered the merchant's debt as paid.

The next day when Miguel went to collect the money, the merchant had disappeared. And now, to compound the bad luck, it was time for the regular examination of his books in Seville.

Again Miguel's luck was running against him. The discrepancy was discovered almost at once, and explanations were of no avail to these petty officials who knew nothing of Miguel's long years of honest service. Too bad, they shrugged; but until this matter was thoroughly investigated, he would have to cool his heels in prison.

Two bailiffs escorted him through long corridors, up many steps, down many more, until they came to a door, behind which there arose a fearful din. The door was opened and Miguel was shoved into an almost lightless room, where he was immediately greeted by a chorus of howls and derisive whistles. So foul was the air he

had to hold his breath, and at first it was so dark he could perceive nothing. Then he made out a crowd of men who had paused in their gambling to scrutinize him. Their glances were hate-filled, their comments full of contempt.

Instinctively, Miguel felt for his sword, but the scabbard was empty. The weapon had been taken from him. Some of the inmates moved menacingly toward him. They saw threads on his doublet where the King's coat-of-arms had been sewn and torn off. But even before they saw that, they had sensed he was not one of them.

"Who are you?" snarled one. "Come on, speak," said another, and he thrust out his jaw threateningly.

Miguel knew when it paid to be defiant, and when it was the better part of valor to give in. There was no sense feuding with a man to whom one murder more or less made no difference. So he told him who he was, and why he was there. He spoke quietly in Castilian, the "King's Spanish." He could have faked the language of the underworld—he had mastered well the Andalusian dialect—but he knew that nothing antagonizes a man more, regardless of his position in life, than if someone pretends to belong to his class when he has no ties with it at all. He was not one of them. There was no point in hiding it. And so he won their confidence.

They moved away and left him to himself for a while, left him to wonder where he was to sit or lie down because of the filth, left him to follow with his eyes the many rats which seemed entirely at home in this dungeon.

After a few days, however, although Miguel took no part in the gambling and the brawling that went on all day long, one man after another sidled over to him to talk—chiefly about his own plight. Once these cutthroats left off their boasting, they were all trembling with fear, for what awaited them was the gallows. As so often before, Miguel was the patient, trusted listener again, though now the stories he heard were stories of pickpockets, bandits, looters and hired murderers.

To these men Miguel could only listen helplessly. He could not give advice, nor say nor do anything that would alter their fates. Their stories filled his heart with sadness. For all he had seen and known of misery and horror, he had not really known men could be so depraved. And yet—and yet—under all the depravity—all the obscenity—they were still humans like himself, trembling with fear before the unknown, seeking somewhere the unique comfort of human sympathy and acceptance.

But now, for all the officials had been so dubious, it turned out Miguel did not need to stay in prison any longer. An examination of his books, by officials still higher than the local men, had proved that all Don Miguel had said was true. He did have a fine record of tax-collection. In fact, it really seemed that whatever his method, it worked exceptionally well. Looking over the books, the officials had discovered taxes paid by grandees and peasants alike whom they had long since dismissed as hopeless.

Miguel was released from prison. Not only was he released, he was given a promotion. From now on, he was to deal with more important estates, in matters involving large sums. The King's officials had given him a resounding vote of confidence!

15

WHICH *relates how the unlucky Don Miguel goes to jail again—but this time writes a book!*

ONCE AGAIN Don Miguel was in the saddle for days on end. Once again he was roaming rugged country, traveling hour after hour to get from one isolated estate to another. Behind him crawled the wagon with the soldiers beside it, guarding its tempting load of coins. On and on he traveled, through the weeks, through the months, through the years. It was eight years since his book had been published in Madrid—nine years—ten. Even longer since the days of the theater and his plays. Did he think of that vanished career, ever, as he rode, stooped and silent at the head of his lonely little procession through the wilderness? Did he think about the books or plays he might have written, if life had taken a different turning? Did he think about books or plays at all—all the old sources of such intellectual stimulation and delight?

There was little time for reading in the life he led now, little opportunity to obtain books or plays or news of them. And rarely, for all the varied people that he talked with, did he meet anyone with whom he could talk of those things. Of course, here and there, in the little towns, on some of the estates, he found people reading the books of chivalry which were still so popular all over Spain—high-flown, extravagant adventures of knights and their squires.

Later, when he wrote of his knight, Don Quixote, whose mind was unbalanced by the too-avid reading of such fictions, he introduced a certain innkeeper who refused to believe such stories could do any harm. "So far as I can see," he said, "there is no better reading in the world. I myself have two or three of them along with some manuscripts, and they have been the very breath of life not only to me, but to many others as well. For in harvest time the reapers gather here in large numbers on feast days, and there are always some among them who can read. One of them will take a book in his hands and thirty or more of us will crowd around and listen to him with so much pleasure that we lose a thousand gray hairs. For my own part, at least, I can say that when I hear of the terrible and furious blows the knights exchange with one another, I feel like dealing a few myself, and could sit there hearing of them day and night."

So, undoubtedly, did many of the people Miguel met defend these high-flown romances, the only books they had or knew. Young girls would say, like the landlord's daughter, "I like to hear about those things—especially when they tell about some lady or other being embraced by her knight under the orange trees . . ."

Miguel would sympathize, of course, and smile—but surely he would have to rally them a little. "But so many of these stories are all the same. Do you never weary of the sameness? And they are so unbelievable—with their enchantments and their wizards. Do you never wish for a book that you could believe from start to finish?"

"Well, perhaps," the people with whom he spoke would say doubtfully. "But then, there are none like that. So meantime we like these stories."

No one can know, of course, just how or when it came to Don Miguel de Cervantes to write a parody of those knightly romances which were the only books he did see scattered across the countryside. No one knows if the idea came to him full-blown, or slowly assembled itself from one vagrant thought after another, as he jogged on and on along the lonely roads. Suppose—suppose, he were to invent a character who *did* believe all the outlandish nonsense of these books. What fun one could have with him! What amazing adventures one could invent for him!

But this was all idle musing to fill the lonely hours. He had no time for writing. He had no private life at all. His hours were the King's. Sunday was the one day of rest and harmless distractions, but anything like a real vacation he did not have in all those years.

It was thirteen years that he rode on the King's business now—fourteen. And the finances of Spain were going from bad to worse. In the beginning of Miguel's appointment he had seen silver. Now, he saw nothing but copper, and even this copper was mixed with tin. And this affected him, especially in one way. Taxes paid in such

coins made his strong boxes very heavy, too heavy for the horses sometimes. Dragging the coins from where they had been paid to the place where they were to be delivered, proved sometimes more costly than the value of the money transported.

Miguel worried about this, and finally he thought of a solution to the problem. He secured the help of a banker, at a strategically situated place. To this man he entrusted his coins during the intervals between his returns to the capital of the district where he worked. It turned out to be a fine plan—a great relief. He could act with more efficiency and faster. In fact, the plan worked so well, for so long, that he could hardly believe it when he rode up to his "banker's" dwelling one day—and found the "banker" had disappeared. Taking with him, of course, all of the cash which Miguel had deposited with him in the course of several months.

"A man more versed in misfortune than verses," Miguel said of himself later. And here was the proof of it again. All he had to show were a number of notes, receipts which had become worthless. The sum involved was so big that Miguel could never restore the money —*three million maravedis*—enough to build a medium-sized palace, or in the buying power of today's American money, about $300,000.

Don Miguel was ordered to return forthwith to Madrid, to face charges of financial irregularity. The possibility that he had been an accomplice of the banker in the affair could not be ruled out until all the facts were investigated.

So again Miguel went to prison. Stolidly, he accepted this injustice. Life was full of such risks. But inasmuch as his conscience was clear, he was sure his imprisonment was only temporary. Since the matter was still under investigation, he was not mistreated or clapped into a dungeon. He was sent to a jail not far from Madrid, where he was given a small cell, with nothing but a bed, a table and a stool. There he awaited the trial of his case, thinking how ironic the whole thing was—he, who had meticulously entered in his ledger every last *maravedi* that passed through his fingers—he was in jail for embezzlement!

When he was brought before the tribunal, he did not doubt his innocence would be quickly proven. But soon he realized with dis-

may that neither reason nor sentiment were playing any role in this case. The only thing these judges cared about was the *letter* of the law. By his negligence he had caused the state to lose a substantial amount of money. On his own, and without the permission of his superiors, he had resorted to a private banker as a middle-man. In so doing, he had trespassed his authority.

This time when Don Miguel was led back to his cell, he knew that he was going to stay for quite a long while with that bed, that table, that chair—and that blank wall before him.

A man indeed versed in misfortune—a man accustomed to prison by now. He had been a prisoner in Algiers—a prisoner, in a sense, in the garrison at Naples—a prisoner of the Inquisition—a prisoner of the state just six years ago. He could have sat down on the single chair and given himself up to melancholy and despair. Perhaps he did, for a while. A man spends his life defending honesty and probity as the only true standards, and time after time he finds them leading him only to trouble. Perhaps he is mad to cling to such a belief. Perhaps, long ago, he should have done as so many he knew had done—simply *pretended* to believe in honesty, and then acted in whatever manner seemed expedient. There are some who have no trouble with such pretense at all. Alas, it would not work for Don Miguel. Whatever the rewards of honesty, he was committed to his belief in it. He had to act as if it were all that it should be.

Act as if—*as if*. And this, perhaps, was the moment when into his mind there suddenly sprang the character who believed in the impossible tales of chivalry—the character of whom he had mused, out on the road. All at once, there he was—real as life—lean, gaunt, gray-haired and mournful—a man who had to act *as if* knighthood were true; because, indeed, it would be beautiful if it were.

He sprang to his feet, and he called to the jailer to bring him paper and quills and ink, and he waited impatiently while the jailer went to fetch them.

At last the paper, the quills, the ink were delivered, and Don Miguel de Cervantes y Saavedra sat down at the rickety table in his cell and began to write.

"In a village of La Mancha, the name of which I have no desire to recall, there lived not so long ago, one of those gentlemen who always have a lance in the rack, an ancient buckler, a skinny nag, and a greyhound for the chase. . . ." The pen hurried along, hesi-

190

tated, stopped, hurried on again. "This gentleman of ours was close on fifty, of a robust constitution, but with little flesh on his bones, and a face that was lean and gaunt. He was noted for his early rising, being very fond of the hunt. They will try to tell you that his surname was Quijada or Quesada—. . ."

So the story began, the story of Quijada or Quesada, who read so many books of chivalry that he decided to go out as a knight himself. "He went out to have a look at his nag, and although the animal had more *cuartos*, or cracks, in its hoof than there are quarters in a real . . . it nonetheless looked to its master like a far better horse than Alexander's Bucephalus. He spent all of four days trying to think up a name for his mount . . . a name worthy of the new order of things . . ." and he finally hit upon Rocinante. "Having found a name for his horse that pleased his fancy, he then desired to do as much for himself, and this required another week, and by the end of that period, he had made up his mind that he was henceforth to be known as Don Quixote!"

And there he was, with a name and a horse, and ready to ride.

Miguel was not a fast writer. Often he sat at the table in the cell, in the position he himself described in the Preface to the finished book. "Paper before me, pen over my ear, elbow on the table, and chin in hand . . ." He was not a fast writer, but there was so much he wanted to say now. For fifteen years he had written nothing, had

191

only wandered and listened and absorbed what people had to say. Now all that he had heard, all that he had observed were rushing into his mind, seeking an outlet.

Because he loved language, every sentence had to be tested, polished and revised before he allowed it to stand. But he was not seeking precious words, or unusual phrasings. Quite the contrary, he was writing plainly now, simply, with transparent clarity. This was new, brand-new. Readers and critics alike were unused to simplicity. What would they make of it when they read, "The sun rose," instead of the customary, "Phoebus harnessed his fiery chariot?" Miguel did not know. He only knew that here at last was the way *he* wanted to write—the way he must write.

His characters too he allowed to talk and act the way human beings talk and act. Every figure was described with the same objective interest, without regard for rank or station. Thus he created live, pulsating human beings, instead of outworn prototypes. Homely women were not necessarily quarrelsome, servants not invariably sly or doltish, innkeepers were not always avid for gain. He drew them as he had seen them in real life—sometimes one way, sometimes another.

Now the days moved on in joy, too short, all too short for Miguel. He wrote on at night when he could persuade the jailer to bring him a candle, and he rose at the first light of morning to get to his writing again.

Did he know he was writing a masterpiece? How absurd! What writer ever knows anything like that about what he is writing? The book he is working on is everything; more real than life itself while he works on it, more real than hunger, or prison walls or anything. Then, when he finishes and the spell breaks—perhaps he *thinks* it a masterpiece, perhaps not.

The world makes its judgment then, and the world's judgment of the book Miguel was writing has long been made. The clear and simple language that he chose? With it Miguel de Cervantes established modern Spanish in a perfection which has not since been surpassed. Just as in England one speaks of Shakespearean English, so it is Cervantes' Spanish in Spain. His people? They marked a decisive change in the general attitude of the artist towards the world. Up to his time, no writer wrote about people as they really were. "Just people" meant a revolutionary discovery.

He wrote the book as a parody of the absurd knighthood-novels of his time, and indeed after the wonderful laughter Don Quixote provoked had swept through the land, it was hard to understand why those romances had appealed to so many for so long. But this does not make up the importance of the book, because to ridicule something and do away with it is a negative action. "Don Quixote" is a positive book—it is the very first book which embraces all walks of life and thus mirrors its time and customs. But Miguel neither blamed nor chided any group or custom. He simply said: This is the way things are. And allowed the reader to form his own conclusions. So—revolutionary without striving to be militant, revelatory without passing judgment, "Don Quixote" was altogether unique in form and conception in its day,—the first modern novel.

It is still unique, and there are those who hold that even as it introduced the modern novel, it encompassed in its theme every subject that has been basic to the novel from that day to this. For underneath the comedy, underneath the racing story, underneath the reflection of "life as it is," it studied something else as well: the whole nature of reality and illusion; and this, in one form or another, has been the study of every modern novel. There are those who say that what Miguel de Cervantes had to say about this subject—oh, not directly, always in terms of that laughing, racing story—sums up some of the best that man has been able to say about that subject since he first began to ponder it.

16

IN WHICH *our unlucky hero finds good luck at last!*

SIX FULL MONTHS Miguel spent on the wobbly chair, writing at a too-small table; then he was acquitted. By that time, the year 1603, he was fifty-six years old, and because of his age, he was not reactivated into the King's service. He retained his title, however; he received his back pay, and was free to retire on a small—a ridiculously small—pension.

But his book, the book he had been working on so eagerly, so devotedly, was not even near to being finished. Almost, now, he regretted the speed of the acquittal. Other times, when there had been no wonderful, demanding task like this, he had been left to languish for months in captivity. Now, when he could really have used the time— Ah well! He simply must find a room elsewhere, in which he could work in peace.

He had not forgotten how unsuitable the house in Madrid was for such a task. But where else could he turn? Perhaps, he mused, the members of his family had grown less contentious. He himself was calmer, and imagined that he could hold aloof from anything that might prove disturbing. So he returned to his old home where his wife and sisters awaited him. His mother was not with them any more; she had died sometime before.

It was not a festive homecoming. After fifteen years of absence, straight out of prison—gray-haired, shabby and worn—he frightened the women. In their simple-mindedness they felt ashamed of him.

It would have been wiser for him to have stayed away. He asked little, but even so his presence disturbed the routine of the household. Each woman, in her own way, found him baffling: his wife, because he shut himself in a cell like a monk and did nothing but write; his sisters, because he seemed a stranger to them, especially when they remembered how he had been as a boy. Still he was the master in the house, the only man left in the family—for Rodrigo was gone now too—perished long since on the field of Flanders.

But even though the women were disappointed in him, they still loved him, and that did them good. It heightened their self-esteem, when, indulgently and good-naturedly they yielded to what they called his whims and caprices. They nagged at him about working so hard, writing so much would ruin his eyes. They reminded him of other obligations, asserting it was even offensive to God Himself to sit there and do nothing but write.

As for Miguel, he smiled and went on as he had always. The nagging, though annoying, could be considered a stimulus, the unimportant but persistent voice of the opposition. He had to have faith in himself, and in the importance of his work, to overcome this weak but stubborn resistance each new day.

Then Miguel decided it would be well if they all moved to Valladolid, where the royal court had recently been re-established. The book was finished at last—a huge great sheaf of manuscript entitled, "The Ingenious Gentleman, Don Quixote de la Mancha." It was important now for Miguel to be situated in the city where, sooner or later, all the influential men of the kingdom put in an appearance. In Valladolid, he hoped he would find a patron for his book.

So they moved to the new capital, and actually the domestic atmosphere improved with the move. Miguel set about looking for someone to whom he could dedicate his book, a sponsor who would then show his appreciation of this honor by paying at least a part of the cost of publication. Without such help it might be difficult to find a publisher.

Miguel's fifteen years of absence had brought many changes. He had few friends left, and none that he knew of who could be of great help. A man who had formerly helped him, The Duke of Sesea, was no longer alive. His early befriender, Monsignore Acquaviva, now General of the Jesuit Order, possessed no worldly goods of his own. Miguel had only one influential friend, the Duke of Lemos, to whom, long ago, he had dedicated his "Beautiful Galatea." But the Duke was in Naples now, and no longer the wealthy man he used to be.

Miguel himself could not help realizing his was an unusual situation. He was no young and promising talent, but a man in his late fifties. His poverty was apparent, and his career plainly drawing to a close. Moreover, there was something a little dubious in this man with a good name, whose feats of heroism dated back some thirty years or more, and whose earlier literary successes had long been forgotten.

But the few friends he had were loyal. They worked hard on his behalf. Finally, as a result of lengthy, involved letters of recommendation and a whole series of behind-the-scenes maneuvers, they managed to gain him an invitation to the Duke of Béjar; Don Miguel would read from his new book, and if this reading found favor, the noble lord might deign to accept his dedication.

The Duke himself was a robust man whose greatest pleasure came from hunting wild boars. His humor was crude, he loved drinking bouts and noisy festivities. When the Lenten season began, he grew melancholy and suffered dearly for his faith.

He was not exactly the sort of man Miguel would have chosen to read his book to, but there was no turning back. Surprisingly enough, however, the Duke had invited an impressive array of high-born ladies and gentlemen to this reading, dignitaries all, who, he felt, might find it amusing to view this queer fellow of a writer near at hand.

So Miguel began his reading before a small circle of quite spoiled people, who expected little but to be entertained. He had carefully chosen his chapters for the benefit of his host—among them the chapter which told "Of the good fortune which the valorous Don Quixote had in the terrifying and never-before-imagined adventure of the windmills, along with other events that deserve to be suitably recorded." He read, too, with all the old-time skill he had acquired as an actor and mime.

Now, as Don Quixote went charging up to the windmills and was sent reeling for the second time, the Duke roared with laughter and slapped his stout knees. Miguel had to read it again for him, he was so delighted—how the mournful knight tilted against the windmills, and was woefully tumbled from his Rocinante.

When Miguel stopped reading, he felt as though several decades of his life had ceased to be. The atmosphere was full of gaiety and warmth, and again he was accepted in a circle of enlightened people, a circle which esteemed him for those qualities which he himself

prized most. Although the Duke himself was no connoisseur of literature, and had no pretensions in that regard, he had surrounded himself with educated people and scholars who *were* able to recognize genuine literary achievement. After the Duke had set the tone, Don Miguel became the main attraction of the gathering. Everyone sought to express appreciation to him, and it is worth noting that those present had listened quite carefully. Unlike the Duke of Béjar, who was chiefly captured by the slapstick of the windmill adventure, they saw in "Don Quixote" more than just a series of tragicomic misadventures.

After the guests had been served an excellent meal, and when the evening drew to a close, the Duke of Béjar went to his strongbox and presented Don Miguel with a suitable sum of money to assure the publication of his book.

With the subsidy, Miguel quickly found a publisher. And after the civil censorship, and above all, after the Church authorities had given their *imprimatur* (which means, "It may be printed") the book went to press. It appeared in the year 1605, when Don Miguel de Cervantes was close to fifty-eight years old.

The booksellers had voiced many doubts and misgivings. They found many things in the book too bold, or too odd. They would have preferred to see a hero who was, externally at least, a handsome knight. After all, tales of attractive heroes had a sure market. But— oh, miracle!—contrary to the expectations of the experts in public taste, and despite its sorry looking hero, the book had an extraordinary success.

Indeed, the presses could not print half the number of volumes sought. The demand rose so insistently that simultaneously presses were set in motion in Madrid and Valencia. Within a few months, "Don Quixote" became the favorite book of the times. The Knight, and his little, round, proverb-quoting squire, Sancho Panza, were real figures to people who had not even seen the book, and their adventures were recounted by many who were themselves unable to read.

Eventually, Don Miguel even made some money from his work; not enough to live a life of ease, but sufficient to dispel immediate worries. He did not ask for more.

All this did not change the rhythm of Miguel's life, however. He was as regular as clockwork, rose long before daybreak, went to Mass, upon his return had a frugal breakfast, and sat down at his desk. With "Don Quixote" launched and on its own now, he had a

whole series of new writing projects which filled his mind and days. If anything, he worked more intensely than ever, and became less and less concerned with the women in his household. Besides, they were used to him now, and his recognition and fame had mellowed their attitudes. Still, they had much to fret about, because in Valladolid it was more complicated to maintain the outward appearance of a respectable family than it had been in Madrid.

Miguel, like many people, lived primarily from the products of his own back garden, and coined money rarely came to hand. He had some money from his books, true; and he also had claims against the government for back pay, and some outstanding arrears from his brother's estate. However, since inflation in Spain had remained unchecked, when the money finally came into his hands, it was worth much less than when it had been due.

But Don Miguel was used to all this. Money had never meant much to him in itself. Altogether he had risen above customary standards, neither misery nor success moved him one way or another, any more. That was probably the main feature of his character by now: an unshakable loyalty to himself—to acting the way he had found to be right; regardless of criticism or praise, he acted *as if* the standards he believed in were proof against any storm—and so, in the end, they were. Only a person who has supreme integrity can achieve this, only one who has learned to listen to his inner voice, and who is prepared to heed it even if it hurts.

He did not know how much more time was allotted to him, and he did not care. He worked indefatigably but without haste. His tempo was governed by the complete confidence that he still had sufficient years ahead to finish his task, even though his body was weak, undermined by privation and age. His complexion was sallow, his hair thin, and few of his teeth were left. He was neglected and undernourished like most of the men of his day, dirty like all his contemporaries; yet his face radiated kindness, and in his eyes a glint of humor always lighted their seriousness.

A group of French scholars, visiting Don Miguel de Cervantes in his house, reported on their encounter: they had found a man who was old, impoverished and sick; yet—to their great amazement—perfectly contented with his fate.

When Don Miguel was sixty-five, he moved once more. The Court had changed place. Now it was Madrid again, this time for good. The journey proved a strain for the weak man whose health was failing. He heeded the warning, and as a sign that he was prepared to step off the stage whenever he would be called, he joined the Trinitarians, a lay branch of the Franciscan Order. It meant no change for him. In a way he had always been more of a monk than anything else.

All he wished for was a little more time and the strength to finish the various works he had begun.

And then what looked like the same old Cervantes' bad luck struck again!

The year was 1614. His "Don Quixote" was ten years old. And suddenly there appeared on the market, "Don Quixote, Part Two." Written by someone else!

It was true that Don Miguel had ended the first volume of the Ingenious Knight's adventures with a hint of more adventures to come. It was true that he had delayed and made excuses when various admirers pressed him for a sequel. But because he had delayed did not mean he never planned to write it. It was only that "Don Quixote" was so very much *sui generis*—one of a kind—that he could not bring himself to dash off a sequel just to have a sequel. Through the years, the Knight's madness had come to have a very special meaning to Miguel himself—the second book of his adventures must say more, much more than the first, not less.

And then came this sequel written by someone named Avellaneda, who had taken it for granted that "Don Quixote, Part Two" would never be written by its original author. The only thing to the credit of this Avellaneda, beside his audacity, is that perhaps we owe it to his self-seeking efforts that the true Part Two of "Don Quixote" came to be written. As for Don Miguel's response to Avellaneda—part of it came in the Prologue to Part Two:

"God bless me, gentle, or, it may be, plebeian reader, how eagerly you must be awaiting this prologue, thinking to find in it vengeful scoldings and vituperations directed against the author of the second Don Quixote. . . . You would perhaps, have me call him an ass, a crackbrain and an upstart, but it is not my intention so to chastise him for his sin. Let him eat it with his bread and have done with it."

He was far angrier at the slurs Avellaneda had cast at his own person for being old and one-handed. "The scars a soldier bears are stars." He had a few jokes to tell which were pertinent to Avellaneda's desire to remain anonymous. And he wound up the Prologue: "This second Part of Don Quixote which I herewith present to you, is cut from the same cloth and by the same craftsman as Part I. In this book I give you Don Quixote continued, and finally, dead and buried, in order that no one may dare testify any further concerning him, for there has been quite enough evidence as it is. It is sufficient that a reputable individual should have chronicled these ingenious acts of madness once and for all, without going into the matter again; for an abundance even of good things causes them to be little esteemed, while scarcity may lend a certain worth to those that are bad."

The rest of his answer to the counterfeiter was the second volume itself, which took eight months of the most intense work to complete—and which was, when finished, even greater than Part I. A deepening of insight, a mellowing, a maturing of values, give it a strength and a humor that are an immortal delight.

In 1615, the completed work went on the press. Few books have been so quickly translated into so many other languages, and hardly any have won the affections of so many different readers. While Don Miguel was alive, it was brought out in France, Italy, England and Germany; in Holland, Poland and Sweden; and later in countless other translations. "Don Quixote" became a symbol, the personification of an age in transition. But more than that, the heroes of the book became a mirror for everyone who read of them. So they are, even down to our own day.

Honors, fame, even a little well-being, were not denied Don Miguel. But they came late, all too late. His work was done, his journey ended.

He had been working, as he always did, though he was bedridden. The candles had burned low without his noticing it. In the early hours of the twentieth of April, 1616, Miguel Cervantes died. No one was present. He was alone in his last hour as he had been throughout his life.

It is said that on the day of his funeral an enormous crowd followed his coffin, all on foot, and that the streets were lined with kneeling men and women, the last reverence of the many for the one. Princes and humble fellows walked side by side; the Bishops of Toledo and Madrid went along with simple friars; the solemn event wiped out all distinctions of rank and made them one great brotherhood of mourners. All of them were under the spell of the mystery of death, yet all were sustained by the inmost knowledge that death is but the bitter gateway to Paradise.

When the *miserere* ceased tolling, the crowd dispersed, and everyone turned toward life again. That was as Cervantes would have wanted it.

Perhaps it is scarcely to be wondered at that Cervantes' grave is unknown. The man who today is honored in Spain with a square or an important street bearing his name in almost every city and hamlet, was for a long time practically forgotten. Of this man himself, to whom hundreds of monuments have been erected, the world knew little indeed. Neither his birthplace nor his grave.

But that can hardly matter. Don Quixote lives on. And as Don Miguel himself said, in the closing words of Part Two, as the chronicler of the tale hung up his pen: "Here shalt thou remain, hung upon this rack by this brass wire. I know not if thou beest well cut or not, O pen of mine, but here thou shalt live for long ages to come, unless some presumptuous and scoundrelly historians should take thee down to profane thee. But ere they do this—say to them as best thou canst . . . Hands off, o'er weening ones . . . For me alone Don Quixote was born, and I for him; it was for him to act, for me to write . . . and we two are one. Farewell!"

17

A LAST WORD *from the author, in which he confesses certain difficulties in getting acquainted with a classic, and advises you how to avoid them!*

FROM EARLIEST CHILDHOOD I had heard about *Don Quixote*. My father talked about the book and praised it constantly. It was one of the first books he had ever read, and his devotion to it had grown through the years. By the time I was a child, he had collected fifty-six editions of *Don Quixote*—some of them huge tomes with many pictures, others modest two-volume affairs with no embellishments. Most cherished of all was the French edition with illustrations by Gustave Doré. Doré, of course, is the illustrator through whose eyes we are most accustomed to visualize the figures of the quaint Knight and his paunchy Squire. Certainly I must have been impressed by the Doré drawings, because there was a family story of my wandering around the house in the middle of the night, proclaiming that I was Don Quixote himself!

Later, however, after I had become a reader, I was rather over-awed by the book. I tiptoed around it, so to speak—afraid to tackle a work which everyone said was one of the greatest books ever written. Such a verdict made me cautious, and it was a long time before I braced myself for the task.

When I finally did get around to reading it, I was disappointed. At that youthful age, I read for suspense and adventure, and I found little suspense in the curious incidents and accidents which befell Don Quixote.

Still, the book kept pursuing me. Some years later I went to Spain, and found myself one day in the province of La Mancha, the very province from which Don Quixote started out. There, right before my eyes, were windmills which looked exactly like the ones with which Don Quixote had battled. Perhaps they were the same ones Cervantes had seen. Some of them were marked with old dates, back to 1650 even, and there is no reason to assume that fifty years before, others like them had not also been in existence. Not only the wind-mills—the whole landscape took me back to the book for much of rural Spain has hardly changed at all since the Arabs left the region. The houses are built the same way, water is still tapped from the same old wells and carried in old-fashioned jars, and the speediest vehicle is still a mule. Certainly the natives know of automobiles and planes, but they are for the rich, far-off city folk, and have no mean-ing in the country.

However, even visiting Don Quixote's home territory did not help me too much in rereading the book. Once too often I had been told, "It's a deep book." Now I looked for depth and wisdom, and did not find them, in their disguise of preposterous adventure.

Curiously enough, it was Mark Twain's *Tom Sawyer* which led me to Cervantes' *Don Quixote*. Born and reared in Europe, I had heard very little about this American classic. I started reading the book only because I had been commissioned to illustrate it. Ap-proaching the book with no prejudices, no preconceptions, I was not only delighted with *Tom Sawyer*—all of a sudden it seemed I understood *Don Quixote* too.

They are much of a kind, these two books. In *Tom Sawyer* as in *Don Quixote*, all sorts of incidents, adventures and funny stories are loosely strung together, without any one central plot. But reading *Tom Sawyer* with this fresh, unprejudiced eye, I saw there was something else in addition. Perhaps I can express it best by quoting an old Chinese philosopher who said, "Walls, floor and a roof make a house, but the nothingness within is the essence of a house." Read-ing *Tom Sawyer* I saw that pranks, incidents and adventures made up the outline of the story, but it was the unwritten *in-between* which was the essence of the story. In that unwritten in-between, the entire great American scene of the middle nineteenth century came alive for me.

Now I went back to *Don Quixote*. This time I read leisurely, with-out any prejudices one way or the other. It was a book written to entertain. I read it for entertainment, and so I discovered it—with all *its* unwritten in-between that brings the Spain of Cervantes' time alive. Without any effort on my part, it got under my skin and made its essence felt, which is the way of all good books.

Times change and tastes differ. Things which our forefathers thought delightful are often rather boring to us. *Don Quixote*, however, has survived 350 years, has been read from one end of the world to the other, has been the favorite of readers of all ages and many civilizations. This, then, is not a passing fad, but a sure sign of quality —for every generation and every individual has found in the book answers to its own questions.

Yes, *Don Quixote* is full of wisdom, but it is not in the form of heavy-worded verdicts pronounced with a solemnly raised index finger. It is of a casual kind in the way of simple observations. If you have the thought of reading it, make sure you have an unabridged copy of the book, because only the full-length version will give you the all-important in-between. Then pick up the book and read it, not because it is great, or because it is a classic—read it only for your pleasure. Don Quixote himself will take care of the rest.

Prentice Hall   copy 1

AUTHOR
R. Busoni

TITLE
The Man Who Was Don Quixote

DATE DUE	BORROWER'S NAME	DATE RETURNED

Reading Service Center
Fresno State College
Fresno, California 93726